WITHDRAWN

VT Coach

career reflections of veterinary teams

ISBN 978-90-5821-8-537   NUR 530

VetCoach: www.vetcoach.info

VetCoach in Facebook: www.facebook.com/vetcoachproject

Printed by Printworks Global Ltd. London/Hong Kong

Disclaimer

VetCoach and VetTeamCoach are private not-profit projects by Dr. Richard C. Nap. The contributions in this book are based on the personal experience of the authors, and reflect their opinions only. They are career reflections presented with the sole objective of helping younger colleagues. The role of this editor is to pass on these messages. The editors and the sponsors do not accept responsibility for the content of the contributions. My advice is to please ignore if you disagree or what does not appeal to you.

Introduction to the first VetTeamCoach book

All members of the veterinary health care teams are important to provide support to the incredibly strong and unshakable Human-Animal-Bond between the family members and their pets. Owners consult the veterinary team by phone or during the visits because they are concerned about the health of their pet and trust the team members to deal with it in a professional and Fear Free™ environment. Our goal is to look after both the "physical" and "emotional" wellbeing of the pets under our care.

The pets have become family members and have entered the hearts and homes of their families. They've moved from the kennel to the kitchen to eat and from the cage to the couch to rest. The health care provided to these pets has to meet the highest quality professional and ethical standards. Collectively, veterinary health care professionals have built personal data bases of knowledge and experience that can serve as a valuable resource for the future. Those team members who have extensive training and many years of in-the-trenches experience have broad overview and specific tactics, tips and strategies to share with young staff members entering the profession and help them to "thrive" and not just "survive" in the greatest profession on earth.

VetTeamCoach collects career learnings from veterinary staff professionals, nurses, technicians, receptionists, managers and shares them with young colleagues. All these staff members, together with the veterinarians, provide high quality veterinary health care on a daily basis to thousands of farm animals and pets.

I have been a supporter of the VetCoach project for veterinary students and young graduates from the beginning and fully support this new VetTeamCoach initiative to reach out to all other members of the veterinary health care teams for the benefit of the pets and animals that give us so much pleasure every day. They deserve the best of our care.

Dr. Marty Becker
"America's veterinarian"

*Great Kiskadee or Benteveo
by NVAC wildlife artist Jim Wilson*

Acknowledgements

First and foremost, I thank all of the contributors for sharing their personal stories. Together they have made a unique collection of career learnings available to the profession. A special thank you to Dr. Carin Smith for her suggestion to make this book. Despite the incredible support by my co-editors Rebecca Rose and Jenifer Sullivan there will be some remaining mistakes. They are all mine.

My warm thanks to Ruud Plaisier About Pets, NL / Welzo Media Productions, NL. It has been a pleasure to work with you and your team again to make this 7th book together! A special thank you to Serge, Todd and Alexis at VCA AH (Veterinary Centers of America Animal Hospitals) for their continued support for this first VetTeamCoach book and for thereby making it possible to generously reach out to all members of the veterinary health care teams.

I thank you the reader for your interest in the VetTeamCoach project. I hope that you will like and get inspired by what you see in this book. If so, please help us promote VetTeamCoach via your networks for the benefit of your colleagues and team members around the world. Please contact me directly with your suggestions for improvements and corrections at > richard@uppertunity.com <

Last but of course not least, I thank my wife Dra. Betina Rama who often tells me I am crazy to work on this project but who continues to be its strongest supporter.

VetTeamCoach, a valuable gift

The Veterinary profession has developed rapidly in recent years, and high levels of specialized veterinary health care are now available to many of our farm animals and pets. The veterinarians have been able to improve the quality of health care products and services thanks to the support of many highly motivated, passionate, and qualified staff members. The support by technicians, nurses, receptionists, managers, and all other hospital team members is essential for veterinary health care centers to deliver owners an optimal health care experience.

The developments and changes throughout the years have shaped the profession and its members. Valuable knowledge and insights about the current high level of services provided are with the team members who have "been-there-done-that". Their collective knowledge and experiences offer a rich source of education for young team members entering the profession. VetTeamCoach is grateful to all the 58 authors of this first-edition VetTeamCoach book. They have dedicated valuable time to share their personal professional career reflections with only one objective: to support the careers of the next generation of veterinary health care professionals.

The VetTeamCoach mission is to bring this unique collection of career insights to the hands (and minds) of as many veterinary health care team members as possible. This would be impossible without the animal health care associations, organizations, and companies that support the project. One person should be mentioned by name: Rebecca Rose, CVT, founder and owner of Catalyst Veterinary Practice Consultants. Without her support, you would not have this book in front of you.

VetTeamCoach is a private, non-profit sub-project of VetCoach (www.vetcoach.info). VetCoach has published more than 11,000 books in five editions for distribution among graduating veterinary students and young veterinary professionals. In 2014, a VetCoach e-book has been added to the VetCoach library and is available via Amazon-Kindle.

We trust that this new project, VetTeamCoach, will receive a warm welcome by the members of the veterinary community and will serve the objective of facilitating and optimizing the careers of many of its junior members.

The editors look forward to receiving your comments and feedback.
Please send to richard@uppertunity.com.
Enjoy this unique collection of golden veterinary health care nuggets!

Dr. Richard C. Nap
Editor

Welcome VCA Animal Hospitals

A successful animal hospital team always strives to provide excellent medical care and exceptional client experience. In order to accomplish this at a high level, the entire hospital staff must understand and support the mission of the hospital. Every employee plays a role in the success of the hospital. We all share the tremendous responsibility of providing medical care and guidance for beloved family members - the pets that our clients care so deeply about. We can't just say, "We practice high quality medicine at our hospital," without being able to back that up. We must ensure that we are truly practicing at today's accepted medical standards, not those from years past.

Leadership and teamwork at all levels in the management team is essential, and the goal is to be progressive through constant education, dedication, communication and adaptation to the changes in our wonderful profession. This is a very exciting time in veterinary medicine, as we have so many newer technologies available for more accurate diagnosis and treatment of medical disorders, and ways to better communicate with our clients; include text messaging, e-mail, and web pages. External factors like on-line reputation management continue to evolve and these require research and effective implementation.

VCA supports you by collaborating with VetTeamcoach. We applaud VetTeamcoach's vision of providing educational resources not only to veterinarians (VetCoach) but to the entire hospital healthcare team.

Dr. Todd Tams

Welcome NAVTA

On behalf of the National Association of Veterinary Technicians in America Board, we are all very excited that VetCoach brought about the VetTeamCoach for all of you. The contributors of this book will inspire you and give you huge insights to their experiences. All of them have already made a huge difference in many veterinary technicians' lives and we have no doubt that they will have an effect on all of you as well.

As students and our future, we want to bring inspiring words and tools of the trade to you to take and build on. We want to help you in any way we can and will be here for you as a resource, professional support, continuing education, your professional voice and help in pushing this profession to what all of us can be proud of.

This is the best profession EVER!

Know that we wish all of you the very best! You are our profession's future and we believe in you!

Julie Legred
Director the National Association
of Veterinary Technicians
in America

Welcome WSAWA

I have always believed that the Vetcoach project was a great concept and was pleased to contribute my thoughts to the original edition. This was focused on new graduates in the profession and contained much wisdom.

However, the profession is much more than that, no matter which branch of the profession we chose we are almost always part of a team. Veterinarians need their support staff to enable them to focus on patient care.
Similarly veterinary nurses, technicians and assistants play a critical role in veterinary practice.
The original editions included much sage advice and this new edition, VetTeamCoach which is focused on the entire practice team will, I am sure, prove beneficial to all.

We have all learned much upon the hard road of life and would love to have known then what we know now.
This valuable tome will help to blunt and shorten some of those life lessons.

Prof. Dr. Colin Burrows
President, World Small Animal Veterinary Association

WORLD VETERINARY
ASSOCIATION

Welcome WVA

On behalf of the World Veterinary Association (WVA), I would like to congratulate the VetCoach Project on the publication of the new book: VetTeamCoach and to express the WVA strong support of this project to share veterinary professional experience and career learnings with new colleagues to the benefit of the veterinary profession, society and animals globally.

The WVA is over one hundred and fifty years old. In April 1863, Professor John Gamgee, from the college of Edinburgh, UK took the initiative to invite professors of veterinary medicine and veterinarians from all over Europe to a general meeting in Germany to discuss and to exchanges ideas on different veterinary topics.

This initiative has grown to what the World Veterinary Association is today, especially due the continued flow of knowledge, information and experience from one generation of veterinarians to another.
WVA follows the ambition of Dr Gamgee to bring veterinarians from all over the world together, to share experiences, to exchange ideas and to join forces for the promotion and development of veterinary profession.

The VetTeamCoach project is an inspiring initiative where young members of the veterinary staff learn and received advice from experienced colleagues that goes beyond the traditional veterinary curriculum. Such life and work related experiences open the eyes for different professional opportunities, original and creative approaches to face challenges and ways to develop further our amazing profession which bring health, welfare and joy to animals and humans.

Yours sincerely,

Prof. Dr. Faouzi Kechrid
President of the World Veterinary Association

INDEX

Authors INDEX

VT Coach

career reflections of veterinary teams

Valarie Adams

1. "Those Sweet Words" (Norah Jones)

I've always loved the flow of words - how they roll off the tongue, the inflections that can be used for effect to deliver a certain timber of emotion, the freedom of expression they provide when trying to convey a certain sentiment or passion. We used to call this a "gift for gab". I shouldn't have been surprised to have this early talent, as my mother always proclaimed I could talk before I walked. Folks with this talent often became top notch sales people (of various vocations) or preachers. While I was neither of these, I still found my talent to be quite an asset early on with my employers, who discovered I could diffuse an irate client or fend off a demanding pet parent or drug rep.

The real benefit to this "gift of gab" wouldn't be fully realized, however, for many years.

Life's hard lessons and twists and turns rendered me rather speechless for a period of time, at a loss for words to express myself in a way that I felt understood, so the period of using my words for creative expression morphed into a slow, quiet drone. I wish I could say that there was some big aha moment, some lightning-strike event, that happened to help me realize how important giving others a voice is. But, it was slow and cumulative, the kind of awakening the seeps into your pores and radiates your heart warm. My years spent in emergency critical care made me aware of the many families that felt they had no ability to express how their hearts were consumed with heaviness trying to figure out how to be the best advocates they could be for their beloved pets.

What I learned was the best way to give them a voice was through EMPATHY and COMPASSION. One can always learn words and become skilled in artful ways to use them, but if they aren't delivered with heartfelt empathy and compassion, they will resonate vacantly and artificially. Speak your words with your soft heart, with honesty, and deliver with empathy and compassion. You will be staying true to yourself, and the pet parents who are entrusting you with their hearts will be grateful.

2. "You're So Vain" (Carly Simon)

Many of us have had the privilege of bearing witness to staggering changes in veterinary medicine over the past decades. Very little has changed, however, when it comes to human nature. It is through a commitment to personal growth that a person becomes less judgmental and fosters a propensity for being open to new ideas and concepts. For some, this comes naturally; for others, this comes slowly with age; and for a few, it never comes at all.

For me, choosing veterinary medicine as a career instead of human medicine was something we used to joke must have happened in utero because it was so deeply ingrained. I felt like I was entering into a club of professionals who shared my sentiments about animals and the Human/Animal Bond. I looked at my colleagues as comrades in arms. As I saw it, we understood the animals in our care. We made this unspoken vow that even though we would never be wealthy, we would be fulfilling our passion of tending to this wonderful group of creatures not of ourselves, like our human counterparts were consigned to do. In my early days in the profession, college did nothing to alter that thought.

The reality, though, is that everyone who goes into veterinary medicine does not feel this way about the profession - and that's not unlike other professions. There will be many areas of the profession where it will be about degrees and hierarchy and who you know and how much money you make. Unfortunately, there continue to be unhealthy environments where those who are learning are not nurtured, where nursing staff members are not appreciated either for their education or for what they uniquely bring to the profession. There will be those situations where old paradigms persist. There will be those people who do not value the opinion of someone without an equal education or experience because they like to feel superior. You might be in a position to decide if "the juice is worth the squeeze."

That doesn't mean you shouldn't continue to work and study hard to continue to learn and grow personally and professionally. At the end of the day, it will be you looking in the mirror at yourself.

3. "Somewhere Between Right and Wrong" (Earl Thomas Conley)

Looking out from the lens of veterinary medicine 41 years ago, I saw the field as black and white, or right and wrong. For instance, we certainly didn't have the pharmaceuticals we have in our arsenal today to treat cancers and chronic diseases. There were few diagnostic tools to diagnose disease processes and surgical approaches were limited. But, the older I get, the more I'm learning to love the color grey, and I believe you will find this a benefit as you make your way through your career. Opening your view to see the landscape through another's lens can give you the oppor-tunity to see a vista with a panoramic view that you wouldn't ordinarily see by the restrictions of black and white - which is as restrictive as right and wrong. The truth as I see it is this: we waste a lot of time defending our positions as being right and the other person wrong. This forces the other guy, your colleague, boss, employee or pet parent, to defend her/his position as being right and proving you wrong. By starting a dialog, by placing no judgment, by staying non-accusatory and putting your listening ears on, you can stop wasting time and start learning.

And, if two or more professionals participate in this activity of not looking at "I'm right and you're wrong," there can be a bona fide exchange of ideas regardless of rank and privilege. The road-blocks in nurturing this environment can be tall, but well worth the effort in the long run. Your task is to keep your horizon as expansive as you can and not narrow the core with the singleminded-ness of right and wrong. Get up close and personal with the color grey.

4. "Spirit in the Sky" (Norman Greenbaum)

Most will agree that religion and spirituality can coexist, so that even if you're a person who does not subscribe to an organized religion, you can still be a person with your individual sense of spirituality. If you can start out with this idea firmly in place, you will serve yourself well when the uncertainties of your career descend upon you… and they will. Fear is your biggest enemy, and the best way to harness your fear is by embracing your spirituality.

Your spiritualism can include making time for enough play to balance out your hard work. Devote time to this. It will make you a more even-handed professional and others will enjoy being around you; but more importantly, YOU will enjoy being around YOU. Your spiritualism should include believing in something other than yourself. Believing in yourself is a grand idea, but, the truth is, you are not the center of the universe. Neither am I. And that's an okay thing. Your spirituality can include surrounding yourself from time to time with good friends and reminding yourself why you participate in something other than your career. Fulfilling your spiritual appetite can come in the form of quiet reflection, perhaps honoring those you love, those you've lost, and those for whom you've helped facilitate these steps. Never ever forget that your spirituality has the ability to feed, nourish, and guide your career. When you put LOVE at the helm, you can never go wrong if you remember to show the same to yourself.

Valarie Adams, CVT, has more than 40 years of experience working in veterinary medicine, with the last 17 years in the emergency/critical care (ECC) specialty. Her graduating class from the Medical Institute of Minnesota was one of the first in the field of veterinary technology. Valarie's pioneering career as a technician provided her with a breadth and depth of different experiences relating to the Human Animal Bond, out of which has emerged a natural development of passion with this focus.

Her journey to learn more about and eventually provide veterinary hospice and palliative care started more than eight years ago. After spending several years researching and learning from mentors in the field, her passion and dream came to life in May 2008, when she created the **Healing Heart Foundation, Inc.** (HHFI), a 501c3 non-profit organization that supports philosophies and partnerships honoring the spirit of the Human Animal Bond. The first program, **Healing Heart Pet Hospice**, is mirrored after human hospice in that veterinary professionals assist pet families with caring for End of Life (EOL) pets in the comfort of their own home surrounded by their loving family. To her knowledge, this is the first program of its kind in the state of Wisconsin. HHFI also sponsors two other programs: **Healing Heart Pet Loss Partnership and Healing Heart Helping Pets Fund.**

Valarie speaks on the topic of hospice care and palliative medicine at conferences across the country and around the world. Additionally, she has written articles for online publication and print, as well as co-authoring a chapter in a book.

Valarie shares a farm with her husband in Wisconsin and says her horses feed her spirituality and keep her grounded. Singing in a rhythm-and-blues band provides a creative outlet and allows her alter ego to come out and play.

Kim Albin

1. Practice safety first. I have been a Veterinary Oncology Technician for a long time. Through my years in practice, the safety standards have changed as well. Unfortunately, the best safety practices are not always implemented due to finances or convenience. I myself have cut corners, been forced to cut corners, or did not have the needed protective equipment.

I have learned to ALWAYS take the time to apply your personal protective equipment, to check your equipment regularly, to clean properly, and to never assume something is clean. I am just as sick as some of my cancer patients. Because of years in this profession and cutting corners, I have DNA changes, I do not make all of my hormones, and I have shortened my life due to exposure to cytotoxic drugs. I have learned to never wear contacts in your eyes while working - they hold anything they come in contact with against your eye. I have learned to never wear perfume, since it can mask the smell of agents in the air. I have learned to not wear makeup, since it can trap carcinogens against your face. I have learned to never wear my work clothing or shoes home - tracking chemotherapy into my house and exposing my children is not my goal. I have learned to use a closed system and a biosafety cabinet that vents to the outside. I have learned that not only do cytotoxic drugs kill cancer, but they change non cancer cells as well.

I have learned the hard way not to just grab that post-chemotherapy dog out of its own urine. Wait to put on your protective equipment, then grab the dog. Even if the dog has been sitting in its own urine for a bit, it can wait a moment or two more for you to be safe. In conclusion, you can NEVER be too safe when it comes to dealing with cytotoxic drugs. Always take the time to protect yourself.

2. Take time to listen and think. When dealing with clients who are angry at the amount of their bill, take a moment to think about what they are really angry about. These clients are probably angry about their pet being sick or something else in their life. Take the time to agree with them, because the bill probably is expensive. You can't

do anything about it and it sucks. Sometimes just getting a conversation going and not arguing helps calm the situation.

3. Never judge. I had a client who sold his home and was living out of his van with his two dogs. He did this so he could have money to treat one of his dogs for cancer. To me, that was a bit over the top, but for him, it wasn't. I had no idea until I asked why he chose to do this. He had never been married, had no kids - just his dogs. His dogs had been with him for years through thick and thin. He spoke of how the dogs would greet him every night when he got home. How they never were upset with him when he was too tired to walk or play with them. How they were always there for him. He felt that at this time, in the time of need for his dog, he could do every-thing to make the dog's last days comfortable and feed him what he wanted when he wanted it. The owner had the money to make the last days for his companion, who was always there for him, fantastic. This owner made his sacrifice for his dog. He said, "I can buy another house, but I can never replace my dog and his love."

You never know why people do what they do and it will humble you to know. So, never judge and always accept.

Kim Albin, LVT, VTS, has been a licensed veterinary technician since 1996. She received her oncology subspecialty license in 2009. Kim has worked in many veterinary clinics across the United States and has assisted in the opening of oncology specialty practices nationwide, including the new veterinary oncology department at Virginia Tech University.

Most recently, Kim has taught oncology courses to the veterinary technician students at Michigan State University, and she serves as proctor of three online veterinary oncology courses.

Kim is primarily a mother to a teenage girl, a wife of 20 years to an eternally teenage man, a USA triathlon coach, and - in her free time - she is a sponsored amateur triathlete.

Deana Baker

Remember there is more than one way to do something. What we have learned in school is the most common way. As long as the basic rules are followed for the procedure, do not try to change it especially if you are a new hire. Wait until you have been in the practice for a while.

Whether you are a new technician or a seasoned pro, do not go into a new practice "with guns a blazing" when taking a new position. Telling long-time people in the practice that they are doing things wrong or that you don't like the way they do things will not help you to become a part of the team. If you have been hired on as a manager, this is very important. Technician managers particularly need to encourage teamwork.

Ask for a working interview if at all possible. You will be enlightened about how the practice is run and whether you would be a good fit. Plus, you will be able to see the hospital layout. For example, having the x-ray system in the treatment room might be a big turn off. It was for me.

If you have a question, ask it, but don't ask your question in front of a client. When working with clients in the exam room or elsewhere, keep them as the center of attention. After all, they are the ones who enhance your paycheck.

Do not use your cell phone at work unless it is for your job. There are a lot of great apps for veterinary medicine. However, personal calls and texting need to be done on your own time. Follow your hospital policy on cell phone use. This might even get you a raise. If you are the manager or employer, you also need to follow hospital policy concerning cell phones. Managers and employers need to be setting an example for the rest of the staff.

If you are going to take a job offer or turn one down, talk to the hiring person directly. Yes, I made that mistake. I talked to the receptionist to turn down a job. Yes, that was very unprofessional of me. Likewise, do not text or email your decision.

Ask if someone will mentor and train you when you're hired. Do this especially if you are a new graduate. Not all practices are run the same way. Everyone uses the computer differently, even if it is the same software.

Honesty is the best policy. Owe up to your mistakes. We all have made some doozies. Anyone who says that they have never made a medication error is either new to the field or lying. I have made some of my best errors with Baytril.

If a calculation looks "funny," either refigure it yourself or have someone double check you. Those darn "floating" decimal points can get you in trouble.

Seasoned technicians and assistants need to help the "newbies." Remember, you had a difficult time placing an IV catheter and restraining that mean cat when you first started. Someone helped you learn. Pay it forward.

Get some type of continuing education every year. It doesn't matter if you need it to keep your credential. Use the CE perk fully if it is a part of your benefit package. Assistants need to do the same.

Keep your credentials current in the state where you work. If your state does not offer credentialing, credential in one that does. It is much easier to transfer credentials to a new state if you move than to retest or redo credentials.

Remember what it feels like to have to pee so badly that you think your eyes have turned yellow? Your patients feel the same way. Take them out at least once during the day, But two to three times is even better. Cats should be given the opportunity to use a litter box. This will keep your patient happier and cleaner. Make sure that it is okay to take the patient out before you do so.

Have a life outside of veterinary medicine. Yes, we are passionate. If your employer feels that you need to work many hours, think about it hard. Saying no thank you will help prevent compassion fatigue and burnout.

Depression is common in most medical fields, including veterinary medicine. If you are feeling depressed or suicidal, please get help. People in the veterinary field have great access to the "good and permanent" means to commit suicide. I know what it's like to lose someone to suicide. One of those people was a wonderful friend and cousin who was a veterinarian.
Yes, euthanasia solution was used. His suicide was very devastating to his staff, his family, his friends, and the community.

Take care of yourself. You will not do your patients, clients, or employer any good if you are burned out. If you need to go to the doctor, go to the doctor. A good employer should realize a healthy person is a productive person. If your employer doesn't get this, work elsewhere.
There is no reason to stay on a job that you are not passionate about. Many practices are desperate for good veterinary technicians and assistants. If you dread going to work, take some time off. Again, a good employer will understand the need to take a vacation or a mental health day.

Deana Baker (Douglas Wyoming) graduated from Eastern Wyoming College in 1991 with a degree in veterinary technology. Since graduation, she has been in practice at a small animal hospital in Cody, Wyoming that also treats exotics.

Deana got into the veterinary profession in a round-about way. She worked as a pet groomer in a small animal practice in Laramie, Wyoming, for five years. She was on-the-job trained and turned out to be a pretty good groomer. She did assistant work and kennels in the winter when grooming was slow. Deana realized that she enjoyed the medicine, so she returned to school. In 2000, Deana sat and took the VTNE. This was the first time that it was offered in Wyoming. She passed the exam with a good score after being out of school for nine years.

Deana is a founding member of the WyVTA (Wyoming Veterinary Technician Association) and is currently serving as President. She became credentialed in 2004, when the WyVTA started credentialing veterinary technicians.

Deana's hobbies include dog training, walking, quilting and sewing, gardening, and spinning chiengora (yarn spun from dog hair) on a drop spindle and spinning wheel. She has just started spinning wool and other natural fibers.

Mary L. Berg

In 1992, I began working with a small veterinary dental research company as an administrative assistant. Before long, the owner of the business recognized my love of animals and my ability to work with them and asked me to start participating in dental studies. Within a few years, I achieved my goal of becoming a Laboratory Animal Technologist (LATG), but even then I felt something was missing, so I enrolled in St. Petersburg College's Online Veterinary Technology Program. Online education was very new at that time. Yes, I had to use dial-up technology to attend class! After completing the program and becoming a Registered Veterinary Technician in Kansas, I was asked to join a group of Veterinary Technicians that were organizing a specialty academy in dentistry. To say the least, I was honored and excited to be included in this group of individuals. In 2006, along with the others from the organizing committee, I received my Veterinary Technician Specialist credential in Dentistry. This designation has opened so many doors for me and advanced my career to the fullest.

Since that time, I have also completed AAHA's Veterinary Management Institute, continued to work in veterinary dental research, been a practice manager at a general practice for more than seven years, served as a room moderator on VSPN, and managed my own consulting company. In 2013, I made the plunge to revitalize my consulting business and dedicate my time to Beyond the Crown Veterinary Education. This was a huge leap of faith and - quite frankly - very scary!

My husband, friends, and colleagues encouraged me to have faith in myself. Becoming my own boss has allowed me to give back to my passion of veterinary medicine by becoming a board member of NAVTA and the Kansas Veterinary Technician Association. It has also given me the time to serve as the Treasurer for both the Academy of Veterinary Dental Technicians and the American Veterinary Dental Society. Recently, I joined Catalyst Veterinary Practice Consultants,

Life experiences as a Veterinary Technician

I recently read a post on Facebook that states: "If it wasn't hard, everyone would do it. It's the hard that makes it great!"
I would love to encourage Veterinary Technicians to realize that anything is possible if you try, but only you can make the changes and accept the challenges.

What have I learned as I have progressed through my veterinary career? Don't ever believe you can't achieve your goals. Some of those goals may take a little longer, but the reward at the end of the journey is priceless. I began my veterinary career quite by accident. I grew up on a Minnesota dairy farm and was forever trying to save a kitten or begging my dad to let me help the veterinarian when he came out to our farm. Eventually, the veterinarian would call the house and ask if I could go along to help deliver a calf at a neighbor's farm. It took me a while after college and following my husband around the world with the U.S. Army before I found my way back to veterinary medicine and my true passion.

along with other leaders in the Veterinary Technician field!

At the same time all these other amazing things were happening in my life, I was asked to be an instructor at Wright Career College's Online Veterinary Technician Program. This was another dream come true as I have always loved teaching. No dial-up Internet this time! I could not be where I am today without believing in the future of veterinary technicians and having amazing support from wonderful friends and colleagues I have met on this fabulous journey!

As busy our lives get, you must have balance in your life. Make time for family and friends, enjoy your hobbies. I enjoy volunteering with the local 4-H clubs in my community, spending time with my family, gardening, and reading (novels, not textbooks!).

My advice to Veterinary Technicians: never pass up an opportunity for continuing education or the chance to advance yourself and your career. If you want to see changes in our profession, it is up to you! Become involved in your local, state, or national Veterinary Technician organization; promote your profession in a positive and professional manner. You never know who you will meet along the way and how those individuals may influence you and help you on your career path. Take pride in yourself and your profession!

Mary L. Berg, *BS, RVT, RLATG, VTS (Dentistry), grew up on a small dairy farm in Southwest Minnesota. She received her B.S. in Biology/Microbiology from South Dakota State University, after which she traveled to many locations worldwide with her military husband. In 1992, they move to Lawrence, Kansas, where she then earned her A.S. in Laboratory Animal Science from Redlands Community College, and her A.S. in Veterinary Technology from St. Petersburg College. She is a charter member of the Academy of Veterinary Dental Technicians and received her Veterinary Technician Specialty in Dentistry in June 2006.*

Mary currently serves as the treasurer of the AVDT and the American Society of Veterinary Dentistry. She is the past president of the KVTA and a member at large of the NAVTA board. Mary worked in research for more than 22 years, specializing in products aimed at improving oral health of companion animals. She was the practice manager and dental technician specialist at Gentle Care Animal Hospital in Lawrence, Kansas, for more than seven years.

Currently, Mary is the president of Beyond the Crown Veterinary Education, a veterinary dental consulting service, and an instructor for Wright Career College. Mary and her husband, Doug, have two sons and live on a farm near Lawrence, Kansas, with a menagerie of animals.

Claudie Berriet

France

It is an integral part of our work.

Know the animals you take care of. A good veterinary nurse must be capable of recognizing an animal who is suffering and help to relieve this suffering and protect the animal from self-trauma by all possible means.

In an emergency, be capable of anticipating and develop a good sense of priorities.

The veterinarian must be able to rely on you to help prepare the equipment needed for whatever treatment might be chosen - even resuscitation, for example. If surgery is called for, the operating room must be prepared early so that everything is ready when the animal arrives.

Here are my working rules and philosophy as a veterinary nurse:

First of all, it is essential to love animals! But loving them is not enough. You must be realistic about what you are capable of doing. From time to time, you even have to accept the fact that treatments are not effective anymore and that "the ultimate solution" is more humane than hopeless overuse of intensive medication.

Keep an eye on everything. In the daily care of the hospitalized animals, a good nurse must verify and re-verify orders at all times. Double check all your dosages so that no mistakes occur in the protocol of care. Keep the animals in your care comfortable and clean - you are responsible for their well-being. Recognize situations that become critical and alert the veterinarian.

Document cases and complete invoices properly. And these are just to name a few things!

Claudie Berriet *(Douarnenez, Bretagne, France, 1968) is currently is the head nurse in Centre Hospitalier Vétérinaire Frégis, Paris, France. In 1991, she became certified as a Veterinary Technician from Institut Bonaparte, Paris. In 1998, she qualified as Veterinary Technician (level 5) from GIPSA - Maisons-Alfort.*

After a short employment in a first-line practice right after graduating, Claudie applied in Frégis in 1992 and has made her entire career in the same hospital, starting with night shifts and then becoming a general nurse. She then specialized in surgery, anesthesia, and intensive care.

For the last eight years, she has been in the position of head nurse, meaning that she teaches and that she coordinates and supervises the work of 17 teams of technicians. She also takes part in veterinary nurse teaching for candidates to the degree of Qualified Veterinary Technician (level 4 & 5). She also has had the opportunity to write a few articles for French technicians' periodicals.

Merrill Bohaning

USA

Bullying in the workplace, it is not just on the playground!

Hopefully, you have not been a victim of bullying at your clinic or hospital. According to Veterinary Team Brief Magazine, up to 75% of veterinary technicians will experience one form of bullying or another during their careers. It is hard to believe that, after all that schooling and training, instead of finding a work environment that practices a total teamwork approach, many individuals will take the approach of wearing down your self-esteem to build themselves up.

If you are not aware of what bullying looks like, the definition of bullying - according to Merriam Webster - is:

1: to treat abusively, 2: to affect by means of force or coercion, 3: to use browbeating language or behavior: BLUSTER

You are probably wondering why I would bring up this particular topic. When I was asked to write an article for this publication, I was asked to write about something within my realm of experience. Since I had recently resigned my position at a well-known veterinary clinic and because the resignation was caused by being subjected to daily periods of bullying, I felt this article might help others.

Early Signs of Bullying, according to Dr. Gary Namie & Dr. Ruth Namie from the Workplace Bullying Institute

You know you've been bullied at work when...
- You feel like throwing up the night before the start of your work week,
- Your frustrated family demands that you stop obsessing about work at home,
- Your doctor asks what could be causing your skyrocketing blood pressure and recent health problems, and tells you to change jobs,
- You feel too ashamed of being controlled by another person at work to tell your spouse or partner,
- All your paid time off is used for "mental health breaks" from the misery,
- Days off are spent exhausted and lifeless, your desire to do anything is gone,
- Your favorite activities and fun with family are no longer appealing or enjoyable,
- You begin to believe that you provoked the workplace cruelty.

When actually at work, you begin to have the following issues...
- You attempt the obviously impossible task of doing a new job without training or time to learn new skills, but that work is never good enough for the boss,
- Surprise meetings are called by your boss with no results other than further humiliation,
- Everything your tormenter does to you is arbitrary and capricious, working a personal agenda that undermines the employer's legitimate business interests,
- Others at work have been told to stop working, talking, or socializing with you,
- You are constantly feeling agitated and anxious, experiencing a sense of doom, waiting for bad things to happen,

- No matter what you do, you are never left alone to do your job without interference,
- People feel justified screaming or yelling at you in front of others, but you are punished if you scream back,
- HR tells you that your harassment isn't illegal, that you have to "work it out between yourselves",
- You finally, firmly confront your tormentor to stop the abusive conduct and you are accused of harassment,
- You are shocked when accused of incompetence, despite a history of objective excellence, typically by someone who cannot do your job,
- Everyone - co-workers, senior bosses, HR - agrees (in person and orally) that your tormentor is a jerk, but there is nothing they will do about it (and later, when you ask for their support, they deny having agreed with you),
- Your request to transfer to an open position under another boss is mysteriously denied.

I realize this list seems overwhelming, and it is hard to imagine these things taking place in a clinic where we all care for animals and love our jobs. But I will tell you that the majority of things listed happened to me and to others I worked with. In fact, there appeared to be some kind of "pecking order" so that one by one the weaker members of the team were bullied out of their jobs until it became my turn.

In a perfect world, I could have gone to my manager, addressed the issue, and gotten resolution. In my case, the manager was just as much a problem as the doctors and other staff. Granted she was new, overwhelmed by the job and the issues going on within the organization. But all of us should absolutely expect protection and counseling should an issue occur within the practice. In my case, even a transfer to another location was denied.

So what can you do? The answer to this question will be tough to swallow. In most cases, the bullying is not going to stop or improve. In fact, by bringing it to light you stand the chance of becoming a target for retaliation. Here are some ideas:

1. 77% of bullying targets will quit or get fired from their positions. So have a backup plan in place when you decide to take action. If you can, quit with grace and professionalism. The temptation to make a decision based on emotion and yell at everyone as you leave can be tough to ignore. But ignore it. Leave with dignity. It will make you feel better and give you a better chance to get another job quickly.

2. You should take action. Do not let this person(s) ruin your career, your health, your family, and your self-esteem. By allowing the bullying to go on, you give the bully more power than he or she deserves.

3. Take care of yourself. You may feel like crawling between the sheets of your bed and never coming out. It is okay to "take a break" for a while. But, eventually, you must pull yourself out of the dark hole you are in and determine your next steps.

Most of all, remember: this is NOT your fault, and you are not alone!! Reach out to friends and family. Possibly get assistance from a physician. Do not be embarrassed, this has happened to us all at one time or another.

My story ends well. After leaving the clinic I worked at, I heard that many others had left. I received phone calls from my fellow workers letting me know their feelings about my departure and how angry they were at the set of circumstances.

I found the strength to move on and follow another dream of mine, which was to start my own company working with animal centered businesses. But that is another article.

Merrill Worden Bohaning *(born Washington DC 1958) is a Certified Veterinary Technician, Certified Mediator/ Negotiator, and highly effective communicator with more than 20 years of successful experience in the private and public sectors using the latest communication practices, tools, and techniques to promote human and animal health goals, resolve disputes, solve problems, provide outstanding customer service, and bring people together as productive teams. Merrill also is certified in Pet First Aid/CPR.*

Merrill's professional experience includes working as a CVT for Banfield® Pet Hospital, as a customer service executive for IBM/ROLM Company, in designing telecom installation strategies for NASA/Johnson Space Center, in constituent services for Senator Kay Hutchinson's Dallas Office, and in designing/ implementing programs on communications security.

Debbie Boone USA

1. The Art of Delegation

When I began managing veterinary practices, I was 29 years old. I had grown up in a family business and thought I knew my way around. Like many in our profession, I was an over-achiever and jumped into my work with both feet. I loved it! But as the years progressed, I gained some insight into leadership and team motivation and found that I was "hogging" all the glory. My staff was wonderful, caring, and smart and I was not allowing them to reach their full potential because I was trying to control every aspect of the work.

Sometimes, the best lessons are learned the hard

way and that is how I learned mine. In 2001, I was diagnosed with breast cancer. This required that I back away from many of my tasks and even be out of the office for six straight weeks after surgery. That is when I experienced my epiphany. My smart, dedicated, well-trained team could do lots of things that I had been holding on to unnecessarily. So I learned to let go. Much to my joy and amazement, the practice ran just fine. Sure, there were some minor glitches, but my now-empowered team was shining and excited with the new responsibility. When I returned to work full time, we kept the momentum rolling by having them keep those additional tasks and fine tuning the training and follow-through so they could continue to grow.

That delegation lesson also found its way into my home life. As a wife of many years, I thought my job at home required me to control all traditional "wifely" duties, like grocery shopping, cooking, and cleaning. When I got sick, my amazing husband took up the slack and became my caregiver. I add this message because - in the veterinary profession - there are so many women who stretch themselves too thin in the name of "having it all" and "perfectionism." I want to say "STOP"! Share the responsibility with your team and your spouse and even your kids. You will all live a happier and more fulfilled life. Sometimes we burn out because we set ourselves on fire.

I am thankful every day for the lessons I learned and grateful that I have a spouse who supports my crazy travel schedule as a consultant by dividing our household duties - sometimes very unevenly in my favor. I work to teach practice owners and team members shared responsibility - we are all in this together and together is always more fun than alone.

2. Fear Not

Over the years, I have certainly been afraid. Fear is necessary to protect us, but fear also can stop us from reaching our full potential as humans. In my experience, one of our biggest "fears" as veterinary team members is the fear of "NO." We automatically assume clients will refuse higher-priced services for their pets, so many times instead of offering our best care we take the safe way and offer plan "B". It is important to remember this: No one ever died from hearing "NO" in an exam room. If we don't offer, the answer will always be "no" by default.

Fear also prevents us from accepting challenges in life. I have seen many new graduates hold back from a difficult case or surgical procedure out of fear they will make a mistake. Sometimes they may even avoid a demanding client.

Obviously, you don't want to harm a patient or alienate a patron, but find a mentor to serve as your life preserver and jump in the water! Mistakes are a natural part of learning. No one is perfect all the time.

Look in new directions and take a chance. For many years, I managed hospitals. Having grown up in business, I was completely in my comfort zone. One day, I was asked to start joining and then facilitating "roundtables." A short time later, I was asked to give a presentation - to more than 500 practice owners! I was terrified! But I took the leap. By taking that chance, I laid the ground work for my current career as a speaker, trainer, and practice coach. Now I seek those scary challenges and appreciate how much I learn and grow from each and every one.

Fear not - take chances - be amazing - there are no do-overs in life.

Debbie Boone, BS, CCS, CVPM, is a self-professed "customer service geek." She began her training in business management and the care of customers while growing up in her family's six restaurants. She laughingly jokes, "My parents were firm believers in child labor," so she started working with the public at the ripe old age of 12.

A love of animals led her to a degree in Animal Science from North Carolina State University. To get her foot in the door to her dream job, she began her career in veterinary medicine as a part time receptionist. Her business, retail, and hospitality background quickly moved her into the position of hospital administration. She managed AAHA-accredited hospitals for 23 years. Her rather unique skill set includes experience with small animal practices, mixed animal practices, specialty hospitals, emergency services, and even shelter management.

Acknowledged as a leader in change implementation, her skills as a trainer and speaker have been utilized by most major animal health manufacturers and distributors to bring value-added services to customers. She is the national instructor for Webster Veterinary Supply's Reception Skills class, where she has trained more than 2,200 front-line team members to give WOW customer service.

In 2009, Debbie opened her business, 2 Manage Vets Consulting, where her focus is to partner with practices in developing extraordinary team communication skills to enhance patient care and in teaching best business practices to increase profits and practice value. She is a member of the VHMA, and is widely published.

Vicky Byard

1. Don't take the first job offered to you just because you feel lucky to have found a job.
That was my first mistake and I made it the day I graduated. There was a practice that I had a relationship with because it is where my best friend took her pets. I saw that they were advertising for help, so I applied and felt lucky when they offered me the position.

I didn't ask for a job description. I didn't shop around to see what was available. I was young and this was easy. I was shy and my self-confidence was pretty low. Consequently, the position I accepted was as a sole tech in a small mom-and-pop practice. I was a glorified animal restrainer. I did no dentistry, no emergency care, no anesthesia, no catheter placements, no drug calculations, no cytology, no behavior counseling. I did, however, clean cages, bathe and dip many dogs, answer phones, sterilize instruments, write out reminder cards, shred volumes and volumes of newspapers for cages, and I napped on the X-ray table when the practice had no appointments and the vets were out of the building.
I was also paid $4.17/hour and had no benefits. There was no health insurance, no sick pay, no vacation days, and no continuing education.
In 1981, we, as graduating technician students,

were told that not every practice offers benefits. So, I felt lucky to have landed a job close to home where I knew the veterinarians. Just between you and me, I didn't think I was worthy of more.

Sometimes the Universe has other plans for you. I may never have left that practice. So, life has a way of helping you make changes you were not capable of making on your own. I was in an auto accident and sustained a hairline fracture of the C-6 and C-7 vertebrae. I had to step away from that position for eight weeks per the orthopedist's orders. As a sole technician, that hampered the normal flow for the practice and I was informed that I needed to return full time within a week of the accident or I would be replaced. Funny, I am actually grateful for that car accident.

2. Always say yes when you are asked to try something new (professionally).
In 1985, I dressed professionally for an interview for a new job. I knew that I was interviewing with the practice owner. His last name was Fox. So, hoping to subliminally land this job, I went to a local tack shop and purchased a fox horn lapel pin for my 1980s preppy blazer. To this day, I believe that pin got me the job that I call home today.

That job was as a Certified Veterinary Technician for an eight-doctor practice. The practice owner was so impressed by the interview that he offered me the supervisor position. I said yes. In hindsight, I was ill prepared and very immature for such a task, but I can't tell you how much I learned and how I grew. I learned to lead by example. I discovered the value of fun and that to keep underpaid staff members, they have to want to come to work. And, most importantly, I learned that I had not been fully utilized in the previous practice and that technicians are capable of so much more. I was capable of so much more. A few years later, Manor College contacted me and asked if I would like to teach in the vet tech program. That sounded terrifying. But, for some reason - probably financial desperation - I said yes.

Only the first class was nerve wracking. I discovered that I LOVED the feeling of the connection with the students. There was something very special about watching the light of understanding flash in their eyes.

After beginning my dentistry training, Dr. Jan Bellows recommended I join a group of stellar technicians from all over the country to create the Academy of Veterinary Dental Technicians. I would have to travel to Las Vegas, alone, to meet and work with a group of technicians I had never met. Despite the fact that my brain was screaming no, my heart and mouth said yes. Through that journey, I have learned much about myself. I thought I had a passion for veterinary dentistry, but I found out that I adore teaching others so that they can provide similar care for their patients.

Because I was courageous enough to say YES, my scope of healing has expanded exponentially. That knowledge has provided great joy in my life and has kept my career and life vibrant and worth living.

3. Seek out any communications training if offered.

I remember thinking to myself, "I want to work with animals. It will be so much better than dealing with people." Despite the fact that I was told on my admission interview at Harcum College that veterinary technology is not an escape from interacting with people, my introverted personality was drawn to the idea of minimizing contact with the two legged species.

Some 20 years later, as part of the Bayer-Technician Advisory Council, I had the opportunity to be exposed to some in-depth communications training. I had no interest in this training, thought it would be a sleep fest and a waste of time. On the contrary, it has been of pivotal importance to my career. As I learned empathy and good listening and communication skills, work life actually became more exciting. As I have become more open to the needs of our clients, I find they trust me on a much deeper level. That is critical when

discussing treatment plans with clients. I find it is easier for an owner to decline care if they don't think YOU care anyway. But, when they know YOU care about them and their pets, they are more apt to be open to discussing options and tailoring care to the needs of the family.

4. Don't be afraid.

For years, I looked at certain traits I possess as admirable. I am dependable, loyal, and conscientious. I am also a perfectionist. That does make for a good employee, but I have wondered of late if those traits were actually good for ME.

I am realizing more and more that those characteristics are deeply rooted in fear and an intense need to please others. One of the benefits of aging is that life has a way of eroding enough layers to show you some hidden gems of change. I do say yes a lot. But, having said yes to some things also lets me experience things I do not want to waste my time with in the future. I now know I enjoy writing what I want to write about. If I am asked again to write on "Computer Applications in Veterinary Medicine," I will say no! I now also know that I do not find any joy in being in a leadership role. I am a great employee and can inspire others to be valuable employees, but leaders have to make hard and fast decisions that affect some for the greater good of the group. That is difficult for me. I can embrace that I am a great worker bee.

One of the greatest gems of change I found recently was the gem of worthiness. "PetED™ Veterinary Education and Training Resources" was a dream of mine. It was a vision I kept denying myself because I felt dreams come true for other people. But I have come to believe that I am worthy of the risk and vulnerability involved. I now know that if PetED™ is a success, that is wonderful but if it is not, I am strong enough to find other "life lesson gems" among the rubble. The experience of living and working toward your life mission is truly delicious.

I try to remind staff and audiences that we chose to go into veterinary medicine. That decision is often made despite friends and family warning us of extraordinary student loan debt, late hours, weekend work, euthanasia, little to no mentoring post-graduation, and the fact that vet medicine is a dirty and trying job. Undeterred by that, you still held your breath hoping to be accepted into veterinary medicine. Well, that means that we have chosen a vocation… not a career. If you break down the word vocation, the Latin root word "vocationem" means a "calling." Those compelled to move toward veterinary medicine do what they do to give deeper meaning to their lives. Remind yourself often that you have chosen a vocation and not a career. That will inform your decisions and attitudes when the call comes in the middle of the night, when the client doesn't medicate that ear, when the owner questions the bill because "all you did was spaded her," when your arm is shoulder deep in a cow while the frigid, subzero wind whips through the barn, and when you have to hold the owner that is grieving the loss of a dearly loved pet because she is a single mom and she can't afford the lifesaving surgery.

You answered a call from deep within you and it is my belief that you have been chosen to take this ride. Treasure every joy and tear it brings to you.

"Our deepest calling is to grow into our own authentic self-hood, whether or not it conforms to some image of who we ought to be. As we do so, we will not only find the joy that every human being seek - we will also find our path of authentic service in the world."

Parker J. Palmer

Vickie Byard, CVT, VTS (Dentistry), CVJ, is a Certified Veterinary Technician with more than 30 years of experience. She has crafted a diversified and exciting career for herself. Vickie has worked at Rau Animal Hospital in Glenside, Pennsylvania, since 1985. Early in her career, she began teaching as an adjunct instructor in the Manor College Veterinary Technology program, while working full-time clinically. In 2006, Vickie became a charter member of the Academy of Veterinary Dental Technicians and she is a past-president of the academy.

In 2008, Vickie was invited to join a group of stellar technicians, the Bayer Technician Advisory Council, interacting with more than 100 "stand-out" technicians mentoring their ability to reach their career goals. Vickie has authored numerous articles and has contributed chapters for veterinary technology books.

In 2010, Vickie was honored as the Veterinary Technician of the Year for the state of Pennsylvania. In 2013, Vickie was given the much esteemed honor of being chosen as NAVTA's Veterinary Technician of the Year. Most recently, she obtained official recognition as a Certified Veterinary Journalist. Although she still works clinically, Vickie is the founder of, and frequent blogger for, PetED™ Veterinary Education and Training Resources, a source for hands-on, in-house training for veterinary practices.

René Carlson USA

1. Learn how to manage emotional boundaries without losing your compassion or ability to empathize.

Veterinarians are especially vulnerable to depression and suicide for a variety of reasons. One of the most difficult stresses for a new practitioner is compassion fatigue. This may be brought on by the inability to treat patients because of the owner's financial limitations or by the death of a patient where she/he might feel some degree of responsibility or guilt for not being able to save the animal for the distraught family. Pet owners can have extremely high expectations of veterinarians that are sometimes exhausting to meet day after day. It took me a long time to realize I can't save them all and that it wasn't my fault the animal suffered in some way. It is not our fault when the beloved family pet is fatally injured by a car or develops terminal cancer, the dairy farmer is having herd mastitis problems or losing calves, or a horse develops colic and/or laminitis. Despite our very best efforts, we can't save them all. But we can

improve the odds, add some quality time, investigate, diagnose, and develop treatment plans for the causes of the problems, develop honest options to finance care, and most importantly, provide the family with trusted support and understanding about their feelings, without losing ourselves in the tragedies indefinitely. Learn to manage your emotional boundaries for your own self-protection.

2. Become active in your professional organizations.

The one thing that has kept me so excited about veterinary medicine literally for decades has been my involvement in organized veterinary medicine, locally and nationally. It keeps me on the cutting edge and provides new experiences, skills, and knowledge that can be used in the workplace - for my benefit and for the benefit of my practice and patients. Organized veterinary medicine introduces you to people from all career paths who constantly remind you why you fell in love with veterinary medicine in the first place - it provides great networking and a supportive community. You develop more confidence as you take on new tasks for your profession, and you may even get some recognition, which most of us appreciate even if we say we don't need or want it. Consider saying yes when asked to do something to which you might otherwise say no because there are always people to assist you along the way. Better yet, let your organizational leadership know you are interested and volunteer. Be courageous enough to challenge yourself beyond your comfort zone. You will be surprised how much you learn and how rewarding it is to be involved.

3. Set deadlines for when you need to go home for the day.

As a new associate, and later as a new clinic owner, I put in long hours. I would see my patients all day, do surgeries as scheduled, and at the end of the day, begin the long process of writing up my records as thoroughly as I could, researching more information on a difficult case, or wading through administrative issues, such as medical decisions about hospital protocols. I would lose track of time and be at the office longer than was really necessary. Then, worse yet, I would bring my work home and either work at the kitchen table on something (like studying for the next day's surgery) or rant to my family about the frustrations of the day. My husband finally started calling every night at 6:00 p.m. to ask when I was coming home. On another occasion, he told me he wasn't lonely when I was gone, but when I was home. Both of those times were eye-opening and I got the message. I changed my work habits.

I wrapped things up by 6:00 p.m. (except for true emergencies) and when I was home (and he was home), I was really home - not just physically, but emotionally as well. When you are home, be home for your family.

4. Invest in good human relations skills.
There was a point when I was quite the worrywart. It was taking over my life, worrying about money, health, work, family, etc. I signed up for a Dale Carnegie Course (advertised as "Stop Worrying and Start Living"). It truly is one of the best things I ever did for myself. Not only did it teach me some skills to manage and totally resolve my intense worrying, but - more importantly - it taught me human relations skills. This skill set is not necessarily the same as communication skills. Human relations skills are what truly helps you know "How to Make Friends and Influence People." It taught me the value of making people feel important: how to engage anyone in conversation by getting them talking about what is important to them and then listening, how to get people excited about new ideas, and how to increase my confidence in expressing my opinions con-structively and tackling new challenges. This is especially helpful in daily clinical practice, both for your clients and your co-workers or employees. If people like you and trust you, they are less likely to sue you. Understanding people and what motivates them and appreciating how they feel is very important to gaining their trust, loyalty, and compliance with your recommendations. Invest in learning those people skills.

René Carlson grew up in Minnesota and attended the College of Veterinary Medicine at the University of Minnesota. After graduating in 1978, she completed a clinical internship in small animal medicine and surgery at the Rowley Memorial Animal Hospital in Springfield, Massachusetts. She was an associate for 18 years in urban small animal hospitals and in rural mixed practices. In 1996, she built her own AAHA-accredited small animal hospital.

She is a past president of the Wisconsin Veterinary Medical Association (1995) and the American Veterinary Medical Association (2012). Because she was willing to accept the new challenges presented to her, she served as the Wisconsin delegate to the AVMA House of Delegates, a Director on the Board of the American Veterinary Medical Foundation, as a member of the AVMA Council on Education for accreditation of veterinary medical programs, and currently serves as the Director of International Affairs for the AVMA.

Kelly Lynn Cronin

1) Go where the wind blows you.
After 20 years in veterinary medicine, my advice is to rely less on a career map. The road less traveled on which you may end up is often the road that is not even found on your GPS. I had a very clear plan for where my life and my career would go. I was finishing my undergraduate in Animal Sciences and then off to vet school and then off to equine practice. Instead, vet school was not in the cards. My life became complete when I discovered that being a veterinary technician made me happier than being a veterinarian ever could.

2) Take pictures.
Regardless of where you are or where you are going, the trip will be amazing.

3) Surround yourself with the smartest people you can find.
Teach everything and anything you can to everyone who will listen. When I became a technician, I was blessed by an incredible support group. I had doctors and technicians who sought to teach new technicians everything about how and why they should practice good medicine. They taught me that I did not want to be just a technician and that in reality there is no such thing as just a technician. I finally knew that everything I learned in school was something that would or could save a life. When I started, there were no veterinary technician specialists. There were technicians who could throw in a catheter from across the room. That is what I wanted to be. Now that I have attained a VTS credential in emergency and critical care, I know that it is exactly that quality of technical skill and knowledge that I have always sought. I credit those who had faith in me. Similarly, paying that faith forward will make our profession great.

4) Don't be good, be great.
A phenomenon we see in veterinary medicine is that we take the best technician or doctor and make them a lead technician or manager. This seldom means that we have the best manager or the best lead technician. When it happened to me, I sought to bridge the gap. I knew nothing about interviewing or human resources. I found the smartest human resources person I knew and I asked, "What's next?" She encouraged me to study and obtain a Professional in Human Resources certification. I knew little about managing, budgets, marketing, or the business end of veterinary medicine, so I asked her again. This time, she pointed me in the direction of a Masters of Business Administration. Good is no longer good enough. Now we have to be great to thrive in our profession.

I can honestly say no road on my career map was business related and when I made the career map, the VTS road did not even exist. My road is not one that I would have been happy with in my "veterinary school or bust brain," but it has taken me to foreign countries, to adventures, and to amazing new friendships. My pictures are of family, friends, lions, tigers, and kangaroos. I can't wait to see yours.

Kelly Lynn Cronin, BS, MBA, RVT, LVT, PHR, has worked as a veterinary technician since 1999. She has performed a wide range of technician responsibilities, from lab technician duties to office manager duties, and from head veterinary technician to technician trainer. She has worked in specialty practices, small animal practices, and emergency clinics.

Kelly Lynn's education and certifications include a Bachelor of Science degree from the University of Wisconsin at Madison (1995-1999), and a Horse Management Certificate from the University of Wisconsin at River Falls (1996). She is a Licensed Veterinary Technician in the state of Alaska and a Registered Veterinary Technician in the state of New Mexico. She earned her Master of Business Administration from the University of Mississippi in 2012 and completed the Professional in Human Resources certification in 2010. Currently, she is an Examinee in the Veterinary Technician Specialty of Emergency and Critical Care. Kelly Lynn has been a key speaker at several state meetings and wrote and published a successful lead technician manual.

Bernadine Cruz USA

It is okay to say you don't know...

I graduated with a DVM from UC Davis, with my brain full of facts and stats, differentials and potential outcomes for a Merck manual full of diseases and conditions, but a paucity of self assurance. My first few months of being an intern at a busy referral practice where I saw office calls and late night emergencies were beyond stressful. I wish I had known as a new graduate that perfection was over-rated.

In the privacy of your own head, it is relatively easy to admit that you don't have all the answers. But this dirty little secret has to be kept to yourself... or does it? It took me years of being a closet self doubter to come to the personal realization that it was okay to admit I didn't know it all.

Medicine and life are not exact sciences. Why do you think they call it the "practice" of medicine? Life is a journey with bumps and detours that can't be anticipated. You are not always going to make the right decision... so get over it! Some failures are more spectacular than others, but as long as you learn from them, all the better. If you keep repeating the same mistakes over and over again, guess what? You're not learning from them. Why? What are you not seeing? What could you do differently to get the outcome you want?

Every day all you can do is put one foot in front of the other. Keep moving forward, learning from successes and those less-than-stellar results. Have patience with yourself. If you do your home-work, if you ask for help, if you admit that you don't know it all, you will get better. There are no short cuts. My first cat spay took me more than three hours, and it dehisced three days later. My surgical complication rate is MUCH better now. I still second guess myself when cases don't go smoothly, but I don't let pride get in my way of learning from life lessons.

It was liberating when I finally was able to look a client in the eyes and say, "Wow, this is a tough case. There are several possible causes and right now I'm not sure what is at the root of your pet's problems, but I will do my best to find out. I'll do some investigating. I'll talk with my colleagues who are more experienced than I am." I expected clients to run out of the exam room screaming to all in earshot that I was a charlatan and tender a complaint to my state veterinary board. The response to my declaration was just the opposite. They often thanked me for my honesty. I was seen not as some egotistical doctor but as a friend. Abject candor, however, is not always best. Tempering your statements may be needed. But always demonstrate sincerity, integrity, and empathy.

Never stop learning. Never stop trying. Remember that it is okay to say "I don't know."

Dr. Bernadine Cruz (1952) graduated from the School of Veterinary Medicine, University of California at Davis (1982). She has been practicing companion animal medicine at Laguna Hills Animal Hospital, in Southern California, for more than 20 years. Dr. Cruz acts as a multi-media consultant for several major veterinary pharmaceutical companies, along with being featured on numerous local and national television shows, such as the Early Show, the Today Show, the Doctors and Inside Edition. Dr. Cruz communicates on a daily basis in more than 3,000 veterinary reception rooms as one of the hosts for PetCare TV. She can be heard on the internet radio show The Pet Doctor, part of PetLifeRadio. com. Dr. Cruz is a certified member of the American Society of Veterinary Journalists. She is one of the AVMA's experts for WebMD's Pet Health Exchange and currently a member of UC Davis School of Veterinary Medicine Dean's Advisory Council.

Jamie Davis   USA

1. The damaging effects of personal relationships with team members:
Starting my career as a young manager meant that the team I was supervising was very similar in age to me. I was managing people who were in a very similar stage in life as I was and who enjoyed a lot of the same things. Even though navigating the landscape of personal and work relationships is tricky for even the most seasoned manager, being essentially a peer to your employees can put an even more difficult twist on things. I've made the mistake of going out to the bars and dance clubs with the team. Becoming "one of the girls" felt natural to me early on, but I quickly realized that I was not able do my job as well when I had these personal experiences with the team.

I wasn't doing my best for myself and my team, and that was not okay with me.

The best advice I have for those struggling with this is to just say no. This does not mean that you can't enjoy getting to know your team through friendly conversation or even attending group events. I think getting to know your team, what motivates them, what their strengths are, and overall learning who they are will allow you to MORE effectively manage them.

You might be thinking, "I have made some of my best friends in veterinary hospitals and I would be miserable if I could not make close friends at work." I have made some great relationships, too, but I have been able to keep those relationships within the walls of the practice. I challenge you to evaluate those relationships you've fostered outside of the office. Have you been able to make the right decisions when it comes to effectively managing that person? Do you worry that you might strain your relationship if you had to have a disciplinary meeting with that person? What if you went out to lunch with your friend/coworker and arrived back late? Would that person be held to the same standard as any other employee? The reality is that it can be very hard to separate the personal from the professional relationship. Not only does having personal relationships make it harder to manage that person, but it makes it easier for your team to call you out on unfair treatment and favoritism. Even though you might feel you are able to keep things separate, the others that you supervise might not feel this way. This can lead to poor relationships between that individual and their teammates, not to mention a strained relationship between you and the team.

It is better for your hospital and team to keep personal relationships to people outside of the practice and to focus on fostering appropriate professional relationships inside the office. Don't make managing a team any harder than it already is by mixing business and pleasure.

2. Being all you can be in your career can sometimes mean change is needed:

Managers in veterinary hospitals are frequently home-grown, meaning they have worked their way through positions within the same hospital and taken on more and more responsibilities over time to eventually take on supervisory and management roles. This type of mentorship, growth, and support can foster a strong loyalty to the practice. Loyalty is great and something we crave in management, however, don't let loyalty stunt your professional growth.

You may also be in a situation where you have worked at different practices due to relocation or came in to veterinary medicine from another industry. My situation is the first. Starting off with the aspiration to become a veterinarian quickly changed into a love for the business side and - having worked in hospitals since high school - it was a no-brainer to stay within this industry. Over the course of developing my skills, I have managed a variety of different practices in different locations. I strongly believe that I am so happy in my career because I was able to make the needed changes to adapt.
Whatever the path that brought you to where you are today, know that you don't have to be stuck in a position that is not using your skills or providing you with the opportunity to grow your skills or responsibility.

Asking yourself where you want to go with your career is essential to evaluating how to get there. We all need to crawl before we can walk and walk before we can run. Expecting to jump into the role of a highly functioning manager immediately is unrealistic. However, if you have the education, drive, and - in some cases - the experience to get the job done, but are not being given the opportunity, you need to do one of two things.

If you are happy at the practice and want to work on this, you'll need to start by communicating with your supervisor or the practice owner. See if the opportunity is there and work toward it. Your practice owner might not be comfortable with you having control of or viewing financial data. Why not ask if it would be possible to see figures as percentages instead of true numbers. Conversely, you might be in a situation where the only way to move forward is to move on to a new opportunity. Don't be afraid of change. A new opportunity with new challenges might be just what you need to take yourself to the next level in your career.

3. The art of listening to your gut… and trusting it!

As you grow and gain experience, you will develop this little voice in your head. I like to call this my "gut". It is that feeling you get when you know that the applicant, while qualified, is not going to be able to perform at the level you need. Or when you have completed a task but know that you really should do it again or do something differently. My advice is to listen to that little voice. And even more, learn to start trusting that voice.

Veterinary medicine is a highly collaborative industry. Doctors consult with other doctors or specialists on cases. Managers and leaders in the practice make contacts and consult with others through networking groups or other members of the management team within the practice. It's why we incorporate systems like peer reviews and working interviews. It's why you are reading this publication!

With all these collaborative efforts, we sometimes forget to rely on our own instincts. You are doing yourself and your practice a disservice if you ignore these gut feelings. In some cases, you are also causing the practice a financial loss. I had a situation where I interviewed a potential team member and felt on the fence about the candidate. I followed our hospital's standard candidate procedures and had the potential hiree perform a working interview - the team liked him. The applicant had the experience we needed and references that checked out. With all that information, I still had a funny feeling that he was not the right person for our practice, but I couldn't put my finger on exactly why. So, I went

against my gut and hired the candidate. After three months, we were still training this individual and repeatedly correcting him on errors he was making. He was unable to work at the level I expected, especially after three months of full-time training. I end up parting ways with this team member and had to start the candidate search again.

Staff onboarding is one of our most costly endeavors. It is worth every penny if the team member you hire works out, but highly costly if the person doesn't work. This scenario turned out to be very costly for my hospital. I wished I would have listened to that little voice. Our gut feeling creeps up often and we stuff it down. Start listening to that voice intently and begin to trust what it is telling you. It might often be the voice of reason that you need to hear.

4. Learn when to take the high road:

Be the bigger person. This is something my parents told me throughout my childhood. I applied this to arguments with my sister, handling bullies at school, and even in romantic relationships. Never did I think this advice would be useful to me in management. Little did I know that my parents gave me one of the keys to management success.

This seems simple at first glance. We are leaders, professionals, mature in our actions, right? Why would we not be the bigger person, or, as I like to think of it now, why would we not take the high road? Well, it is simple. We take time and consideration with all the decisions we make in practice and when support staff doesn't agree, we get offended. After all, we are human. We don't want to defend our actions and decisions, to explain all the things that went into the decision, especially when we deal with difficult decisions on team members. We care, we are not insensitive bosses! I'm not saying that we don't want to communicate things with our team or be dishonest in anyway. Don't forget that some situations will be confidential in nature and can't be discussed.

We first have to look at how this feedback is

obtained. Sometimes it is formal, other times hearsay or gossip is the source. Entertaining the latter can cause a manipulative environment that can allow team members to use gossip to get things they want. It also can create a feeling of uncertainty for staff if the leadership team is constantly defending their actions and displaying a lack of confidence.

Deciphering what things to discuss further with the team is the first step. Topics that relate to other team members' performance, work status, or wages are confidential and should never be discussed. Other topics will depend on the practice owner's view point, but certain financial figures might need to be kept confidential. Lastly,

refrain from discussing plans for the practice until they come to fruition. The team might feel they are constantly being set up for disappointment when plans for the hospital don't pan out.

Don't always jump to defend your decisions when you get feedback from the team that they didn't agree with your decisions. Evaluate the situation and, as hard as it can be sometimes, take the high road. Instead, focus your efforts on creating a culture of communication and support between the team and management.

Jamie Davis, *CVPM (Pittsburgh, Pennsylvania, 1977) began her veterinary career in 1995 working in veterinary hospitals during high school. Starting as a part-time kennel attendant, she worked her way through a variety of support staff positions in patient and client care, aspiring to become a veterinarian. After she graduated from the University of Arizona with a bachelor's degree in Animal Science in 2000, she realized that her passion was more for the business of the veterinary hospital versus the medicine. Starting as a client service representative in a Florida specialty hospital later that same year, she quickly took on office management, practice management, and now hospital administration. In line with her goal of becoming a leading hospital manager, she earned her Veterinary Hospital Management certificate in 2007 and became a Certified Veterinary Practice Manager in 2008.*

Jamie currently works as a hospital administrator in Aurora, Colorado, in a thriving three-doctor practice. She has written articles for varies veterinary publications, lectured on practice management, and has served on the AAHA board of directors. Jamie believes that the most important thing she can do is to help mentor other veterinary hospital managers to give back to this wonderful profession. She aspires to be involved on more professional boards, as well as to own her own veterinary hospital in the next 10 years.

During her free time, Jamie enjoys spending time with her husband and two daughters, watching reality TV, cooking, and sewing.

Tina DeVictoria

Many people choose this field because they love animals and perhaps also do not want to work with people, but our four-legged friends do not come in on their own. Even if you do not consider yourself a people person, I recommend working on your communication skills from the moment you have a job interview and everyday throughout your career. When teaching a new team member or when explaining a procedure or lab result to a pet owner, remember that they do not have your level of experience - and perhaps they have no experience at all with medicine. If you feel you are at risk of losing them in an explanation, ask if they are following you. If you fear you may offend someone by breaking the information down too much, ask them what experience they have had before or what their background is. We are a team; from the doctor and technician to the pet owner and their furry friend, we must work together to make sure we are all on the same page.

Throughout my career, I have come across several skills that have made me a valuable and more efficient technician. Certainly, some of these skills are technical and hands on, such as mastering the placement of a female urinary catheter, drawing blood from the cranial vena cava on a ferret, or performing a complete abdominal ultrasound. But the one skill that I find to be the most important is actually not a hands-on skill at all, and has little to do with direct patient care; it has to do with communication. Being a good communicator can make the difference between a patient receiving the proper care or not because the pet owner did not understand instructions. It can bridge the gap between the white coat and the lay person. It can determine whether you have solidified a client for life or whether they will go to the animal hospital down the road next time. It can also make the difference between a new team member succeeding or failing.

Communication with pet owners and with your own team members is critical to becoming a strong technician and professional person.

Some days in the animal hospital are hard. I remember one day in my emergency hospital when we had seven euthanasias! One of those euthanasias was a dog that had been hit by a car. The man who owned this dog, a massive, strong man who worked as a corrections officer, was inconsolable. On another occasion, a family brought in their 2-year-old Portuguese Water Dog, hysterical because she had just died suddenly. Upon examination, she had a whole apple lodged in the back of her throat. And worse, one time the police brought in an emaciated dog with a prong collar lacerating his skin at every point around his neck; he was the bait animal used in a dog fighting ring. We all have horror stories to share, and they are hard.

There are other parts of our job that are hard as well, like trying to draw blood from an emaciated, 20-year-old cat, or restraining a dog that outweighs you, or explaining to pet owners why this sudden disease process is not only life threatening within 48 hours, but it will cost $2,000 to $3,000 to save their pet. Oh, and it is too late to apply for pet insurance.

There is one thing that I find to be the hardest thing, but I try to remind myself every single day to work on it, and that is to not judge people. Have you ever had a client bring in a pet and say, "My cat hasn't been eating for about a week, maybe 10 days." In your head, you're thinking, "Wow, this person is horrible! Who waits 10 days to bring in their sick cat??" It is easy to pass judgment on someone, but we have to remember that we often do not know anything about our clients. We do not know what kind of home life or work life they have, or what responsibilities they have, and yes, on occasion there are things in their lives that are more important than their pets sometimes. As technicians, we have an abundance of compassion for our patients, but we need to work hard - and believe me, it is challenging - to also have compassion for our clients. If you found out that the pet owner whose cat hadn't eaten in 10 days was also mom to two developmentally disabled children and she lost her husband to cancer last month, would you feel badly? I urge everyone to remember daily to not judge people when you don't know anything about their situation in life. Our role is often to be the advocate for the pet, which can make it hard to not judge someone for seeming to make a poor decision on care, but the truth is that we must also take care of the client to ensure the proper care for the patient. We should also try not to change our re-commendations based on what we judge about a client. For example, you may be tempted to change what you recommend to the client who comes in with a Louis Vuitton bag and Manolo Blahnik shoes versus the client who brought their cat to the vet in a taxi and does not have a credit card. You may be surprised who will do the most they can for their pets. Always recommend the best medicine (that's our job) and let the owner make the financial decisions on the level of care (that's their job).

Do you long to make a life-long career out of being a veterinary technician? Do you wonder what more you can do in your field to advance? My advice: never say no to an opportunity, WRITE every time you have a chance, and get involved!

"Never say NO" has been something that has helped me move forward in my career. Here is an example: have you ever been sent for continuing education and your employer asks you to talk about what you learned at the next staff meeting? Do you fear speaking in public so much you consider calling in sick on the day of that meeting? Don't! Take the opportunity to talk about what you have learned. It will help you in several ways. One is that by studying up to give that talk, you will have solidified that new knowledge within yourself. You also may find that speaking is not so bad when you talk about something that interests you. Do not run away from the opportunity!

Writing is another way to advance, particularly if you want to get your name out in the profession but public speaking or lecturing frightens you. Did you have an interesting case at work? Start by writing a case report for the benefit of your staff. Research the condition and write about the nursing goals, disease process, the diagnostics and treatments, and even critique the management of the case by your team. This can benefit you in many ways. First off, if nothing else, you gain a better understanding of the condition you wrote about. It also will help to educate your own team on that condition, and what better way to learn than with an actual case you had? If you and your team enjoy this, consider creating a monthly in-house newsletter and give everyone an opportunity to contribute. You could even post the issues on your practice's website for the benefit of your clients. Another benefit is it can help you hone your skills as a writer. There are many writing outlets in our field, such as journals. Some journals will even pay for articles. Some online teaching outlets utilize written transcripts for class so if you enjoy doing the research and writing, you could even teach online without ever having to talk!

Getting involved may be the best advice I could give on trying to advance in your career. If you are pressed for time, start small. Join a committee with your state tech organization. This lets you get your feet wet learning what responsibilities the state association has and what type of role you could take on, yet it will not overwhelm you with additional responsibilities. It is a great way for you to network with other technicians and assistants in your state, and perhaps even beyond, such as with NAVTA or a VTS organization.

Tina DeVictoria, *BS, CVT, VTS (Clinical Practice—Canine/Feline), was born in Ewing, New Jersey in 1982. Tina attended Rutgers University, Cook College and obtained her BS in Animal Science with a concentration in Pre-Veterinary Medicine in 2005. She originally aspired to become a veterinarian, but discovered the unique, challenging, and rewarding position of veterinary technician.*

Tina has worked in small animal general practice, as well as emergency services and research facilities. She currently works at The Animal Hospital at Kingston and Blawenburg, a progressive small animal practice in central New Jersey. In addition to clinical practice, Tina teaches online with VSPN.org and at Mercer County Community College in their NAVTA-approved veterinary assistant program. She also has published several magazine articles.

Katherine Dobbs USA

1. My Parents Were Right: Get a Bachelor's Degree

Mom and Dad, I swear, I was headed toward a bachelor's degree when I completed high school and entered Texas A&M University with a major in Wildlife Science. Somewhere between watching videos of wrestling alligators and learning DOS computer programming, I lost my way. It did not appear that I was headed toward the life I dreamed of, which at the time was studying lions out on the savannah (any wild cat would have worked, however). At some point, it dawned on me that not many people get PAID to do that type of work. Plus, I didn't really feel like I fit in with the other people in that major; they were a little strange. So halfway through my four-year-plan, I bailed out of the university and found myself in Houston, working for a veterinary clinic, when the Tomball College program in Veterinary Technology began. I was working at an Emergency Clinic, my first job in vet medicine. The first time I saw a dog come in through emergency with its eye popped out, I nearly died. But I hung on, and not long after I went to work for a small, one-DVM, day practice. I had found my calling, and successfully finished my associate's degree in applied science by taking mostly night classes, and passed the state and national boards to become an RVT. A dozen years later, I realized my parents were right when they had encouraged me to complete my bachelor's degree. While it wasn't necessary to have a degree to become an RVT or get a job working in patient care or client services, it was necessary when I wanted to expand to practice management and considered teaching. It matters even more now when I feel the pull toward an MBA or MHA, knowing that if I just had that bachelor's degree under my belt, I would be back in school as we speak. Now we're graduating lots of veterinary "technologists", those who have a four-year degree AND their vet tech credentials. Smart people, wish it was more common place back when I was in school. It would be opening doors that right now that I am merely knocking on.

2. Mixing Work and Pleasure: Becoming a Mom

There were two things I knew back when I was young: I wanted to work with animals, and I wanted to be a mom. Pets fulfilled my maternal urges for a while, but eventually I felt the pull to have a human baby. At the time, I was working at a specialty referral practice where I typically put in four long days - 12,14 hours each - per week. When I felt it was time to become a mom, my first thought was "I'm going to have to quit my job!" That was painful, because I absolutely loved my job and couldn't see myself doing anything else.

So I decided to slow down, and take it step by step. Sure, I could work during my pregnancy, that wasn't too difficult (fortunately, I was no longer involved in much patient care, but was working as a client liaison instead). With a month to go until the baby's due date, I exited my practice for a bit. As a new mom, I managed to get back to work after three months off, and continued to breast feed by taking pumping breaks from the floor (and tying up the employee bathroom!).

Sure, there were many nights I would come home and my baby would be asleep already, her other parent having tended to her needs. That was hard. But then there were my days off, when I could spend the entire day just being a mom. It was a good trade. My daughter entered full-time daycare at three months old, and it was a good place for her. If you find people who care, a baby doesn't mind getting a bottle from someone other than mom! As my daughter grew up, my revised goal became to have an eight-hour work day by the time she entered school, when after-school events

would become important. As it so happened, about that time our practice was ready to expand and move me into the first full-time management position in the organization. I was also ready for my career to change focus; it worked for us both. My schedule was then "mom-friendly", and I never had any regrets… I was able to mix work that I loved and the pleasure of being a mom.

3. Management: Ready? Or Not!

Thinking about making a change to practice management? In my experience, and from many colleagues I've met, management is less of a career "jump" and more of a "gradual lean." It kind of sneaks up on you, really. One day, you're asked to do something vaguely "managerial," like scheduling the staff, and before you know it, you're asked to have "the talk" with a troublesome employee, or be the problem solver for the client issues, or learn how to administer health insurance benefits. Guess what? You're now in management!

Nope, no one ever asked you, really, you just failed to refuse the tasks that one by one were piled on top of you. You may not even have a management title, and most certainly, even if you did get a raise, it wasn't enough to compensate for the headaches you now have to handle. The first and best lesson I ever learned was shortly after I became "management," and was evaluated by one practice owner for my work "on the floor" and another practice owner for my work as a "manager" of others. On the floor, no problem, I was excelling as usual… I loved that part of my work! But as a manager, I had a few things to learn, and the first was uttered right then and there at the table, when the second practice owner said, "It's not your fault, but it IS your problem." It was one of those sky-opening-up-and-chorus-of-angels-singing type of moments, and I knew inherently that he spoke the truth. I was no longer in control of my own performance, because I would ultimately be evaluated on how "my" employees performed. Hmm, I don't remember signing that clause! Had I realized the full extent and meaning of those words, I would have run from the place screaming; but alas, over the next many years, the meaning would sink in deeper and deeper.

Now, as a "consultant" (meaning I get to work with even MORE bosses!), I teach this concept on a regular basis to those considering a move into management. It's a tough lesson to learn. Maybe this is why management feels so much like parenthood; with kids, they typically cause the problems, yet as a parent, it is still YOUR responsibility to clean it up!

Katherine Dobbs, RVT, CVPM, PHR, began as a Registered Veterinary Technician, graduating from Tomball College in 1992. She then held positions in veterinary technology and client services in general practice and referral (specialty/emergency) practice. In 2006, she became a Certified Veterinary Practice Manager (CVPM) through the Veterinary Hospital Managers Association (VHMA). Also in 2006, Katherine founded the Veterinary Emergency and Specialty Practice Association (VESPA), a professional organization that worked to meet the unique needs of those managing in emergency and specialty medicine. In 2008, she created interFace Veterinary HR Systems, LLC, a consulting company that focuses on professional development and performance management in the realm of human resources.

Katherine became a Professional in Human Resources (PHR) in June 2008, furthering her studies of how to help the people involved in veterinary medicine. She became a Compassion Fatigue Specialist in 2009, and a Certified Compassion Fatigue Educator in 2013. Katherine has been published in various veterinary journals in the United States, UK, and Canada, and has published three books through AAHA Press. She teaches on the Veterinary Support Personnel Network (VSPN), and her public speaking experience includes many national, regional, and state meetings and conferences. Katherine was voted the 82nd Annual Western Veterinary Conference Practice Management Continuing Educator of the Year in 2010.

Michelle Franko USA

1. Spending the majority of my career in human medicine - human organ and tissue donation - I thought that I had a rock solid soul. As you can imagine, asking family members to sign documents giving their permission to someone they just met to remove their loved ones organs and tissues is gut wrenching. But I was the solid one of our group - I was the one that could keep my emotions under control and be very appropriate with the family. So when it came time for me to have clients sign euthanasia documents for their pet, I knew that I would be able to draw on that hidden strength, right? Wrong! There is nothing harder than seeing a tough biker guy break down and cry over the loss of his Tea Cup Yorkie. There's nothing worse than seeing a grown woman cry over the loss of her Golden Retriever, who was there for her when she went through her chemo-therapy. I have been with families who have lost

young children, parents and best friends. I have been with people who are so grief stricken and so angry that they could not reason. But I could handle it - I was the strong one. That is why I was there. But this… this was something new. I have learned that most people take comfort in seeing your tears, too. It gives them peace to know that you cared about their four-legged family member, just like they have.

2. When I moved to North Carolina, I had every intention of working with a large Ophthalmology practice. After all, I had spent more than 20 years in medicine and that's where I wanted to stay. I took (not sent) resumes to all of the multi-specialty practices within 15 miles of my home, which numbered 25. No one was hiring. Well, no one was hiring someone with my salary require-ments. My experience was "exceptional," but not affordable. Thinking that it would only be for "a few months," I took a position at a local veterinary hospital - to tell you the truth, I was desperate - I needed a job. Now, I could have gone into the interview and told the DVM that he could keep his $9/hour job - I was used to making $80K a year! But as I sat there, I kept telling myself, "You need this, it is just a spring board to something better, other doors will open." So I took the $9/hour graciously, along with the manual to the hospital's computer program and started working that following Monday. Ten years later, I am at the same hospital and I love what I do. I don't supervise 20 other technicians or 10 DVMs, nor do I have that stress. I am helping those who cannot speak for themselves and guiding their owners through difficult and joyous times. I have come to realize that the "door" I was looking for opened for me 10 years ago because I am doing what I have always wanted to do.

3. Working with animals can be great, stressful, enjoyable, trying, heartbreaking… working with humans can be the same - and some of those feelings are accentuated when you don't agree. You don't agree on medical care, working hours, prices for services, or who has the best college football team… yes, I said the best college football team. I bleed Maize and Blue (for those who aren't Big 10 fans, those are the colors for the University of Michigan Wolverines). My DVM went to Michigan State (Michigan State Spartans); needless to say, we are rivals and the college football season is our battle field. My DVM and I are a month apart in age; we went to college at the same time and grew up knowing our school's greatest players and coaches. We have fun during the season picking at one another about the most recent stats and scores. Well, one fine day my DVM decided he was going to take a few days off and left the office to the staff. Yes, we promised to clean, label, check stock… all the things a wonderful staff does when the DVM is out of the office. We were so devoted to our practice that we decided to paint the office… the entire office… in the beautiful colors of Maize and Blue. That was five years ago. He hasn't taken that much time off since. I wonder why? Oh, the paint scheme is intact. Does this make me a more successful person? Maybe not, but it makes everyone smile when they hear my story.

Michelle Franko *(Lockport, New York, 1963) grew up in Riverview, Michigan (20 miles south of Detroit). She attended Wayne State University majoring in pre-med studies. Michelle obtained her license as a Certified Ophthalmic Technician in 1986 from the Kresge Eye Institute and began traveling the country working for large ophthalmic practices. Michelle moved to Las Vegas, Nevada, in 1989 and attended the University of Nevada, Las Vegas to pursue studies in English. While there - working for two multi-doctor, multi-specialty clinics, she found her way into the human organ/tissue transplantation services. Michelle obtained numerous certificates involving human organ/tissue recovery while working for the Nevada Donor Network.*

From Las Vegas, she moved to Stone Mountain, Georgia, where she managed the technical staff of a

10-doctor, 20-Technician/Assistant multi-specialty multi-location ophthalmology practice. Michelle moved back to Michigan for a year after the passing of her Grandfather, where she took a year sabbatical.

After moving to Kannapolis, North Carolina in 2004, a local veterinary practice gave her a chance to fulfill her dream of working with animals. In June 2014, she will be celebrating her 10th year at the China Grove Animal Hospital. Michelle will be sitting for her Certified Veterinary Practice Manager certificate in 2014-2015.She has also been a respected breeder of Vosmaeri Eclectus Parrots and American Staffordshire Terriers (although, not at the same time).

Jennifer Henne

1. It's okay to say I don't know:
As technicians, we attend school and strive to know all the material and get perfect grades. We are constantly tested on what we know and are expected to know everything. Then we graduate, become employed, and want to impress our new practice. We go along for the first days thinking everything is going great, and then a case comes in that we have never seen before or someone asks us to run a test we have never even heard of. At these times, it is okay to say, "I don't know what this is or I have never done this before." We are so programmed to know everything and always be right that sometimes it is hard to say I don't know. The field that we are in is constantly growing and evolving, that's the great thing about it. So don't be afraid to ask questions and get out of your comfort zone. I worked in an ICU for several years along side other great technicians. I had a co-worker who worked with me for several months and one day finally said, "I know this may sound like a crazy question, but what does CRI stand for?" I was blown away that this person was so afraid to look bad or be wrong that it took her a few months of working together for her to ask me that question. I realized right then that I wanted to make sure I was a person who was open so others could ask me questions, and I also wanted to be a person who asks questions and says I don't know. I don't want to be that person who has to be right all the time, I want to be open to all information and not afraid to say when I don't know the answer to the question. Great technicians are always asking questions and striving to learn new information.

2. Everyone on the team is important
As a new graduate, it is important to remember that everyone on the team is a valuable member. Sometimes we get put into a roll and assume that others are beneath us, but this is something that can get you into trouble. Assuming that you can only learn from a technician or a doctor is very close-minded. You can learn great communication skills from the receptionist who has been at the practice for a decade, or new dog training techniques from the kennel worker who has an interest in behavior and training. I have met a lot of close-minded technicians who think everyone else other than the doctors are beneath them.

Those technicians may be great at some aspects of their job, but they are not very well rounded. Stopping by and saying hi to the groomer and asking her for a few pointers on how she trims feet could save you sometime down the road when you need to trim a foot for a laceration.

It is important to view everyone as being on the same team working toward the same goals. A suggestion that you could make is doing some team-building activities, such as coming up with a mission statement for the hospital.

The department that I currently work in decided to encourage teamwork by doing just this. We all came up with a mission statement, and it was great to see everyone's contributions and what he or she feels is important. It brought our team together and we had something at the end that we were all proud of and could read every day. This helped our department in ways I could not believe, it proved how important everyone is to the practice.

3. Euthanasia is tough, death is tough

When I was in tech school, we discussed euthanasia. I knew patients would die, but in school we never really had to see it up close and personal. You can talk about it or think you are prepared for it but when it actually happens, it is okay to be upset. I remember how hard it was for me when I had a patient in ICU that I had been working with for several days code and not survive. I thought I was prepared, I had all the training on death and what happens to the body, but I was not prepared for the emotional effect it had.

When a friend of mine was shadowing in a private practice, she watched a euthanasia. She had to step away for a little because she knew what was happening, but she was not prepared to see the doctor push the medication and watch the animal pass. We can only have so much training, but watching a patient code or be euthanized is hard. And that is okay; it is okay to shed a tear while in the room with the clients who are euthanizing their 13-year-old Lab. It is okay to be upset when you lose a patient you care about. We get so caught up in trying to save everything and don't always come to the realization that it is also okay to let them go, and it is okay to grieve about that. I am not saying that an owner should be consoling you, but I am saying it is okay to shed a tear and feel compassion for that owner. Or it is okay for you to step out and take a few minutes after that patient you have been working with codes. We chose to work in the veterinary medicine profession to help our patients; it is okay to grieve for their loss.

Jennifer Henne has been working in veterinary medicine since she was 13 years old. She worked at a busy mixed animal practice in Pennsylvania through high school and then moved to Ohio.
She is a graduate of the Columbus State Community College Veterinary Technician Program. While attending school, she worked at a small animal practice as a kennel worker, bather, front desk worker, and veterinary assistant. She worked at this practice for more than five years.

Jennifer currently is a Registered Veterinary Technician at The Ohio State University Veterinary Medical Center, where she has worked since 2006. She originally worked in the Emergency and Critical Care Department for five and a half years, when she transferred and began working in the Community Practice and Dentistry Department.

Aside from her regular duties at OSU, Jennifer currently lectures and assists in labs for the dental club. She also runs the Pet Sitter program, where undergraduate students in the Pre-Veterinary Club come into the Veterinary Hospital and give attention to and sit with patients in the ICU and Oncology departments. She also helps run the OSU Veterinary Outreach Program, which provides veterinary care to under-privileged seniors. She currently resides in Columbus, Ohio, with her husband, two dogs, one house cat, four barn cats, and one pot-bellied pig.

Deanna Herfel

the profession (zoo keepers or vet techs) and don't really know what goes on day to day. Loving animals is not always enough. When you are in school, use this opportunity to see the different specialties. Take advantage of the conferences; most offer free admission or charge only a small fee to attend as students. Select internships that will expose you to a variety of things, not just a place you want to work. Most importantly, ask questions!

One job that is important and used daily is blood draws. Get comfortable holding and manipulating a syringe with one hand. I had an instructor hand me a 3cc syringe and tell me to keep it in my pocket, then during down time, I could practice holding and pulling the plunger over and over with just one hand. When that becomes easy, move up to a bigger syringe.
I know it sounds silly, but it really does help!!

I've worked in a couple of zoo settings (12 years) and with a small animal practice (15+ years).
My first recommendation is for a person to really learn about our profession before entering school. Shadow and interview people in the job you think you want to do. People have limited contact with

And don't be afraid to say "I don't know" or "I'm not comfortable with this."
Those who don't speak up do make mistakes or get bit.

Mrs. Deanna Herfel graduated from The Ohio State University with a Bachelor of Science. While in school, she spent summers at the San Diego Wild Animal Park (now called the San Diego Zoo Safari Park) working in different areas of animal operations. After graduating, she began her career as a Mammal Keeper. In her 10 years with the Park, she worked with a variety of animals, including gorillas, rhinos, antelope, and other hoof stock. In the Zoo's nursery, she helped raise orphan animals. As part of her job, she also presented papers at National Conferences and was part of the team that wrote the keeper training program. After a job transfer moved the family to Ohio, she worked at the local zoo for two years and continued her education with a degree in Applied Science at Columbus State Community College. She began her new career as a Registered Veterinary Technician in 1999.

She has been working at Suburban Animal Clinic in Columbus, Ohio, for the past 15 years and as a supervisor for more than 13 years. Suburban is an AAHA hospital and the best in the area!!

She currently lives in Gahanna, Ohio, with her husband and furry family. She has two children, Emily (in her 3rd year of medical school) and Nic (a sophomore at the University of Cincinnati).

VT$Coach 48 career reflections of veterinary teams

Debbie Hill USA

Certification - Is It for You?

I entered the veterinary field as a receptionist for a small veterinary clinic in Denver. Good people skills and a desire to solve problems made up for the total lack of experience with animals. The next five years were spent learning the basics of the veterinary world. Moving back to Florida allowed me to apply for an office manager position with a veterinarian with broader vision. The title of office manager that I brought from that small clinic was very different from the job I was under-taking. Opening a large hospital from the ground up meant that I would be taking responsibility for more than customer service and billing. I sought

every opportunity for continuing education and was thankfully working for a veterinarian who allowed me to grow.

Five years later, my husband was transferred and I went to work for another practice. The owner of this practice asked that I join the Veterinary Hospital Managers Association with the goal of attaining a CVPM certification. Attending the winter VHMA meeting offered my first exposure to the Certified Veterinary Practice Manager program. With no college education, this seemed beyond me but encouragement from my practice owner, great colleagues, and family led me to delve deeper.

Deciding to send for the application to see what exactly was involved in this certification led me to a course at the local junior college to get my feet wet. Marketing 101 proved to be the turning point in the decision to pursue certification. Taking courses that are relevant to your everyday work made it much more interesting to get that college credit. While the hospital grew, I continued the college courses and any management conferences that could be found, both nationally and locally.

In October 2005, I sat for the CVPM exam and passed. My advice to others considering certification is that you will be surprised at what you can do and the amount of encouragement that is in this field. Go for it!

Debbie Hill, CVPM, PHR, is the full-time hospital administrator for a veterinarian with four small animal practices in Florida, an adjunct instructor for Patterson Veterinary University - Management, a frequent writer on management topics, and a speaker at veterinary management conferences, including ACVC (Atlantic Coast Veterinary Conference), FVMA (Florida Veterinary Medical Association), VHMA (Veterinary Hospital Managers Association), WWVC (Wild West Veterinary Conference), and local manager groups around the country.

Debbie entered the veterinary field as a receptionist at a small animal clinic in Denver in 1989. She was fortunate to attend a wide variety of management CE courses through the American Animal Hospital

Association (AAHA), including Veterinary Management Development School (VMDS) and Veterinary Management Institute (VMI) at Purdue University. Attending multiple management conferences regularly gives her a well-rounded view of veterinary management.

In 2005, she attained certification as a Certified Veterinary Practice Manager and in 2011 attained her PHR (Professional in Human Resources) through the Society of Human Resources Management. She sits on the Board of Directors for VHMA and is the liaison for the CVPM Board.

She is a mixed-media artist (anything with ink and paper) and Bible class teacher who enjoys time with her husband of 40 years, their three daughters, three sons-in-law, two schnauzers, three grandchildren and Maggie, the grand dachshund. It's challenging work, but a great life.

Jamie Holms

A distinguished colleague and friend asked me one day what my end goal was. I didn't miss a beat. "Dying without regrets" was and is my answer. That is my end game and how I've lived my life. It's also how I've practiced medicine for the past 15 years.

In February, a cat bit me. She bit me on my right hand pinkie finger close to, but not in, the first joint. It was a small bite - looked like a scratch. I cleaned it well and carried on (you know, like we do). Within 12 hours, I knew I was headed for

surgery. Within 24 hours, I was admitted to the hospital and four hours later I was on the surgery table. I developed supperative tenosynovitis and had to have aggressive surgery followed by hospitalization and around the clock antibiotics. "It's not so bad," I kept trying to tell myself. I actually had this same surgery eight years ago from a cat bite to the index finger on the same hand. I recovered really well. That is, I recovered really well eight years ago. This time, I struggled. Hospitalization was mentally, emotionally, and physically fatiguing. The antibiotics took their toll on my GI system, while sleep deprivation took out my immune system and all of my reserves. The day after my discharge from the hospital, I suffered an anaphylactic reaction to the antibiotics. During the course of my treatment, I had seven different antibiotics, and they had no idea what had finally tipped the balance. I was treated and recovered but the new caveat to my returning to work was that I couldn't work around animals or be around any antibiotics until they found out which of the antibiotics I'm allergic to. Did I mention I'm an ICU and Emergency Technician who worked the graveyard shift at a 27-doctor practice in the Bay Area? Avoiding animals and antibiotics was not exactly an option for me.

I've reacted to two of the four antibiotics they've tested (ampicillin sulbactam and cefepime) and my next allergy test has been deferred until the cough that developed from the allergic response subsides. Each time the allergist sees me, she says "It's your choice, but it's really time to change careers." She's not alone: the surgeon, the physical therapist, and every nurse who worked on me during my stay at the hospital told me the same thing. How could I go on? Teching, in some ways, is all I know. It's all I've ever wanted to do. I moved more than 50 miles just to work at this particular hospital. My career can't be over! I wanted to pursue my VTS, I wanted to… I feel that sinking regret; that worsening sense of defeat. I was undone, by a cat.

Sitting at home catching up on all the television I never got to watch because I was too tired wasn't enough. I needed to make a difference. When I proposed using my light-duty time to trial a "charge audit position" I'd been trying to sell management on for a few months, I was excited to be presented with the opportunity. It's a tedious task, poring over the treatment sheets, the computer record, the lab notes, the radiology requests, and the ultrasound reports, and cross referencing all of the results. It's far more than I bargained for, and I'm happier than I've been in a long time. This is a completely different challenge. I've met it head on and exceeded all expectations (especially my own).

It's been 14 weeks. Although that cat has a lot to answer for, I regret nothing.

Jamie Holms, RVT, CPT1, (Long Beach, California, 1977) has worked in the veterinary field since 1998, and graduated from Veterinary Allied Staffing Education in Sacramento in 2008. Her experience includes large and small animal medicine, shelter medicine, exotics and wildlife, and behavior. Jamie is currently employed as a Registered Veterinary Technician in the Intensive Care Unit at Adobe Animal Hospital in Los Altos, California (www.adobe-animal.com) and is involved in technician student mentorship and revenue retention projects.

Jamie regularly teaches CPR for Cover Your K9 (www.coveryourk9.org), a non-profit organization that provides K9 police and military officers with bulletproof vests, heat detectors, and trauma kits, as well as teaching human partners how to provide first aid in the field. She also leads a bandaging clinic for the Foothill Community College technician program's annual fundraising event, Pet Ready.

In addition to emergency medicine, Jamie's special interests include compassion fatigue support and awareness. She currently serves the California RVT Association as a Board Member and manages their social media. She has served on the California Veterinary Board as a Subject Matter Expert in the development of the RVT exam and the new California law exam.

Carol Hudecek

Veterinary medicine has a high burnout rate and we, as technicians, are no exception to this. We work long hours, deal with many difficult cases, and often neglect our mental well-being. If there is one thing I wish I had been told from the start of my career it would be this: you need to have a life outside of veterinary medicine. Find something that brings you joy that you can use as an outlet for the daily stress of your job. Being a Veterinary Technician is part of who you are, but it shouldn't define who you are. As the years go by, it becomes more and more important to find a balance in life outside of this job. I have discovered that my outlet is running. Running relieves my stress, rejuvenates me, and puts life into perspective for me every time I go out. Most importantly, I look forward to running and it allows me to leave behind the stress of my day and refocus on being a great technician tomorrow. You need to find something outside of your career as a Veterinary

Technician that you look forward to doing and that mentally invigorates you.
I guarantee it will make you a happier technician.

One of the most important decisions you will make in your career is where you work. In an effort to save even one person from misery, I offer the following advice: when interviewing for a technician position, ask questions. Ask the obvious questions, such as schedule, policies, benefits, pay scale, opportunity for advancement, etc. But don't be afraid to ask the hard questions as well. How do people get along, what is the work environment like, what is the turnover rate? Pay attention to the interactions of the staff during a working interview. Don't be afraid to pull people aside and have a one-on-one talk with them about what the job is really like. If you are not offered a working interview, insist on one. This is your chance to truly see the dynamics of your potential place of employment. Keep in mind that you are going to be spending a significant amount of time in that building with those people. Being a member of a team is all about dynamics and there are going to be personality types that just don't mix well. If you sense red flags or have doubts during a working interview, that is your chance to decline an offer before it's too late. The alternative is to accept a position without knowing all the facts and discovering later on that you are miserable. Don't feel obligated to accept a job just because you have an offer. It is perfectly acceptable for you to turn down an offer if all of the pieces don't fit. In the end, you are the one who has to live with your decision. Had I realized just how important it is to ask questions during an interview process, I could've saved myself some misery in the beginning of my career being in an environment that didn't fit me.

Having a mentor can be one of the most beneficial factors for your career. That person could shape the path for your entire career and awaken within you dreams and skills you never thought you had. It could also, as in my case, turn into a wonderful friendship that has benefits that reach far beyond your job. I had the fortunate experience of finding a mentor very early on in my career. Her name is Jessi Miller and she is the RVT who was in charge of my training at my very first clinic. I was fresh out of school when she took me under her wing. The year that I spent under her supervision profoundly shaped the technician I have become. Jessi is absolutely phenomenal with anesthesia and was in charge of surgery for the clinic.

I admired the gentleness she had for every patient and the immense amount of patience she displayed. That great patience of hers carried over into her teaching me the ropes of being a technician. I was in awe of her confidence, her vast knowledge about everything involving surgery, and the respect that clients and co-workers alike had for her. I can trace my passion for anesthesia directly to her, for without her guidance I might still be that newly graduated technician who was petrified of anesthesia.

The fact that I now teach anesthesia is a reflection of the impact she had on me. Because of her, I also have the goal of attaining my VTS in anesthesia. Whether either one of us realized it at the time, she was my mentor and provided me with the best foundation I could have conceivably hoped for to start my career. If I can give any newly graduated technician just one piece of crucial advice it would be to find a mentor. An experienced technician has invaluable information to share with you and pearls of wisdom that you won't get from a textbook. Take the time to listen to them, learn from them, and appreciate the knowledge they are willing to pass on to you.

As a final piece of advice, I encourage you to take chances. Don't ever pass up an opportunity just because you think you can't handle it. When I found out that Baker College was looking for instructors, I was just two years out of school and was apprehensive about applying. My first thought was, "I'm not qualified to do this." But there was an opening for an anesthesia instructor and my love for anesthesia outweighed my fear. I applied for the position and made it all the way through to the final interview. I was offered the position, but was unable to accept due to scheduling conflicts with the clinic I was working at. As fate would have it, the program director contacted me almost a year later wanting me for the position. I was able to work out a schedule everyone could agree with and took the job. I have been teaching for three years now and can't imagine not doing it. I absolutely love introducing students to anesthesia and watching their confidence grow as the light bulbs go off in their heads. Being there for that moment when they finally "get it" is priceless.

And I would've missed out on all of it if I hadn't taken a chance and applied for the position. If an opportunity falls into your lap, don't be afraid to pursue it because you never know what doors it may open up for you.

Carol Hudecek *(1978) was born in rural northern Indiana. She graduated (Anthropology and History) from Ball State University in 2001 and spent a few years doing grant-funded work in the field of Biological Anthropology. She made the decision to change careers and graduated from the Vet Tech Institute at International Business College, Fort Wayne, Indiana, with an Associate Degree in Veterinary Technology in 2008.*

Since graduation, Carol has worked in a handful of small animal clinics in Indiana and Michigan. During this time, she developed a love for anesthesia and has made this the primary focus of her career. Carol is a Licensed Veterinary Technician at the Columbia Animal Clinic in Brooklyn, Michigan, and serves as an Adjunct Instructor at Baker College, Jackson, Michigan (Advanced Surgical Lab and Surgical Nursing Lab). She teaches anesthesia to senior technician students and supervises them during their 10-week surgical rotation lab.

Liz Hughston

When I was a little girl, all I ever wanted to be was a veterinarian. I wanted to work with animals, help them, take care of them. Ever since I was able to pronounce the word, whenever anyone asked me what I wanted to be as I grew up, I always said, "A veterinarian!"

When I was 17, I had the opportunity to attend a summer program for high school students at Harvard University. I thought it would be the perfect opportunity to get a head start on my college requirements and signed up for an Introductory Biology class. The class was challenging, with lab work that I certainly had not had the opportunity to do at my very small high school. I found myself reaching for the most obvious or easiest conclusions derived from my data collection. When these conclusions weren't correct, I was frustrated. I began to question my career choice. I decided that good doctors can't always pick the easiest or most obvious conclusion and, therefore, I would never be a good doctor. I looked around for what else I was good at and decided to pursue a degree in English Literature and then Education.

As I look back at that time in my life, I realize now that good doctors are trained to look beyond the obvious conclusions and dig deeper to find diagnoses. I know that my decision to abandon my dream was born of frustration and disappointment in myself. Unfortunately there was no one in my life I could turn to at that age to counsel me otherwise. I was a hardheaded and stubborn child to whom things, particularly in school, had always come easily and I did not have the tools to deal with anything less than complete success.

But the beautiful end to this story is that I didn't become a veterinarian; because if I had, I would have missed out on my true calling: veterinary nursing. If I had pursued veterinary school, I would never have realized that I'm not interested in doing surgery or delivering prognoses. I am most inspired by providing care, TLC, and support to veterinary patients and their families. I have gotten more out of being a veterinary technician than I think I ever would have if I had become a veterinarian. I am thankful for the experience of frustration that led me down a very winding path to where I am standing now.

I am in the treatment area of my very first veterinary job and I am trying to place an IV catheter. Frustration is building as I poke and miss, poke and miss, and then have to pass it off to another technician while I restrain. Later in the day, I ask the head technician if she ever felt the same frustration that I was feeling: the nagging worry that my hands would never be in the right place; that my fingers wouldn't do what I want them to; that I would never successfully place an IV catheter. The tech looked at me and said, "I never felt that way. I was always just able to do it." My heart sank. I went home that night depressed, dejected, and thinking I had made a huge mistake. Is this something that should come naturally to me? If it isn't natural, will I ever be any good at it? Why was I going to school to learn to be a veterinary technician when I clearly wasn't meant for it?

Luckily for me, I live with a sane and rational person - my husband - who listened to me vent about my day and set me straight: everyone goes through a time when they're just learning something and can't get it right, but not everyone remembers that feeling. And he was right. I kept at it.

Even when the techs at my internship clinic were frustrated, I pushed for the chance to at least try to get blood, or place the catheter, or intubate that dog or cat. And the more I practiced, the better I got.

Eventually, I left that first job for a hospital that gave me the chance to learn in a very busy environment, giving me lots of opportunity to practice. In my first clinic, we placed two or three IV catheters a day. In the ICU in my new hospital, we might place two or three IV catheters in an hour, giving me lots of opportunities to try. On top of being busy, the other, more experienced techs at my new practice were encouraging, helpful, and loved to teach. It was a match made in heaven!

I have been at that busy practice for more than eight years and have had the opportunity to do amazing things that would never have been possible if I had stayed at the first clinic or if I had given up. When I'm at work, I look around the ICU - at all the patients we are caring for - and I have the feeling that I am exactly where I belong and I'm doing exactly what I had always been meant to do. What a tremendous feeling!

Now I pay that experience forward by encouraging and teaching new generations of veterinary technology students as they intern at our hospital. And when a new tech asks me how I felt when I first started, I remember that first head tech, and I remember how disheartened she made me feel. My immediate response is always, "Of course I felt that way! Everyone does and if they tell you differently, they're lying. But the key is to keep with it, keep practicing, keep learning, and keep believing you can do it." To paraphrase Thomas Watson, founder of IBM, if you want to succeed at anything, first you have to fail a lot. And even though failure is difficult, each one teaches you what you need to be successful. The key is to not give up!

Liz Hughston, RVT, CVT, VTS (SAIM, ECC), (1970) was born in San Francisco, California. As a child, she always thought she would grow up to be a veterinarian but various experiences led her to abandon that dream. Liz graduated with a degree in English from UCLA in 1992 and went on to complete a Master's Degree in Education the next year. After graduation, Liz worked for the Santa Clara County Bar Association as the Fee Arbitration Coordinator. After four years, she accepted a position as the Executive Assistant to the Chairman and CEO of Siebel Systems, Inc., a software company in San Mateo, California.

After her career in professional administration, Liz returned to her first love - veterinary medicine - graduating from the Foothill College Veterinary Technician Program and becoming registered in California as a Registered Veterinary Technician in 2006. In 2012, Liz was certified as a VTS in both Small Animal Internal Medicine and Emergency and Critical Care.

She is currently a Senior Emergency/ICU Technician at Adobe Animal Hospital in Los Altos (www. adobe-animal.com), spending most of her time in the intensive care unit while also triaging and treating emergent patients. She is a member of CaRVTA, NAVTA, AIMVT/ACVIM, AVECCT/VECCS, IVAPM, and IAAHPC. In 2013, she received the inaugural RVT of the Year Award, presented by CaRVTA. Liz currently lives in San Jose, California, with her husband, three dogs, and one cat.

Amy Johnson

As I was thinking about what knowledge or experience I would like to highlight for anyone considering a career in the veterinary industry, especially veterinary technicians, I came up with three key concepts that I feel strongly about.

1. When getting into the veterinary technology field, it is important to know that you are not on the fast track to vet school. The two are very distinct positions within the veterinary profession. I do not believe everyone getting into the field understands the differences. Day one of technician training we learn what we can and cannot do as veterinary technicians, but we don't always get into the nuances of the two positions. The technicians have the most hands-on experience with the animals and diagnostic testing. We are truly "in the trenches."

I know so many people, including myself, who have enrolled in technician programs thinking, "This will get me into veterinary school with no problem." I started my schooling and not only realized that being a technician was not going to move me up the admission list at my chosen vet school, but that vet school was not really what I wanted after all. Students also need to understand that course credits will not transfer or cut any time off from a veterinary program. It is important to realize that many of us do not aspire to be veterinarians; we love what we are and what we do. I hate to hear people say, "You are (or even I am) JUST a technician." I have chosen to be a technician. This is the field I want to be in and I won't feel like less of a professional because I do not want to be a veterinarian.

2. Veterinary technicians do not spend their days playing with puppies and kittens. There are many people who love animals and think this would be the perfect position. What most of us would like people to know about our days is we work hard! This is a medical field that involves math, science, and holding a patient's life in your hands. We are educated professionals who take pride in the quality of our work and our knowledge base. Veterinary medicine is disgusting and gross. We work with bodily fluids, wounds, and bugs. We get wet, dirty, sweaty, and sore. Veterinary medicine is hard on your body and, unfortunately, on many days hard on your soul. We lose our patients, our pets, and our friends. We grieve with the owners, even if we don't know them well. Because of this, we do take that moment to smell the puppy breath, cuddle the adorable kitten, or rejoice in the life that we helped save. There is just as much triumph as there is pain. We love what we do and we don't do it for any other reason than the satisfaction the job brings for us.

3. There are so many different things you can do with this degree. I think one of the most important jobs I have as an instructor is to let my students know the whole world that is open to them as veterinary professionals. We have students who come in thinking they can work in a small animal practice or a large animal practice and that's it. I hear so often there is no room for advancement.

In reality, though, there are so many opportunities open to anyone with this degree.

The specialty medicine fields are growing through many organizations and are attracting more and more technicians. Veterinary technicians have opportunities in small, large, and exotic animal practices, as well as emergency, specialty practices, and veterinary teaching hospitals. They can work as sales representatives, in the pharmaceutical industry, biomedical research, shelters, zoos, reference labs, and veterinary pet insurance companies. The list is endless. This field experiences so much burn out and many leave the industry all together. The best way to avoid having to leave a field you love is to re-invent yourself within it. If you don't like what you are doing, find something else. Do not ever close a door, burn a bridge, or become bitter. Move on and find what brought you into the profession to begin with.

Amy Johnson, BS, AAS, CVT, RLATG, graduated from the University of Nebraska at Omaha in 1996 with a Bachelor of Science degree in Biology. After working in the biomedical research field, she then returned to school at Bel-Rea Institute of Animal Technology in 1999 to get her Associate's degree in Applied Science in Veterinary Technology. Amy has worked in many facets of the veterinary profession, including as a receptionist, veterinary assistant, veterinary technician, laboratory animal/research technician, and veterinary technician instructor. She received her specialization as a Laboratory Animal Technologist in 2008.

Amy has been working as an instructor since 2002 and currently teaches at Bel-Rea while living outside of Denver, Colorado. She also has been instructing and writing online continuing education courses for VetMedTeam since 2009 and has written a small animal pathology textbook for veterinary technicians coming out in 2014. At Bel-Rea, Amy teaches clinical pathology labs, Medical Chemistry, Laboratory Animal

Medicine, and Small Animal Pathology. Her other duties include maintaining the small exotic mammal colonies, IACUC chair, and USDA Liaison.

Stith Keiser   USA

Want to make a difference in the lives of your patients and clients? My best piece of advice is to remember that veterinary medicine is a business and we convey our passion for what we do not only through the quality of medicine we practice, but by the experience we offer our clients and the contributions we make to our team. In our profession, we still at times almost think of profit as a bad thing. One lesson we learned from the recession is that if we can't keep our practices healthy, we can't deliver the level of medicine we desire, hire the quality of staff we deserve, or invest in the community like we should. Whether you're a new associate or support staff team member, I encourage you to actively look for ways to contribute to the practice's health - whether it's through stepping into a leadership role, initiating better client education, or launching a new service that will benefit your practice. For example, as I look at veterinarians we have hired at our practices over the past two years, each had something specific they could bring to the table. One associate had a passion for dentistry and worked with our support staff to train them not only on the technical aspect, but also on how to educate clients. We had another, in one of our mixed animal practices, who was passionate about small ruminant medicine. Before we agreed to hire her, we worked with her to create a "business plan" for adding this service area, ensuring it made sense for both her and the practice. Whether your interests lay in small, mixed, or large animal medicine, finding a niche you're passionate about and willing to grow will make you more valuable to the practice and allow you to have an even larger positive impact on the profession we love.

I once read an article by General Colin Powell regarding leadership and decision making. One particular piece of advice that stood out to me was his recommendation regarding data collection and decision making. He said, "Once the information is in the 40 to 70 range, go with your gut." General Powell's advice is don't take action if you have only enough information to give you less than a 40 percent chance of being right, but don't wait until you have enough facts to be 100 percent sure, because by then it is almost always too late. Roughly six months after I graduated from my undergraduate program, I had the opportunity to launch my own veterinary consulting business. Four years after launching it, I sold it to a veterinary association and have gone on to partner in a few veterinary practices. As I look back upon the fortuitous events that got me where I am today, I've learned a few lessons, in addition to General Powell's.

1. Surround yourself with people who are smarter and more talented than you. This sounds easy, but many in the veterinary profession are Type A personalities and - whether we like to admit it or not - we can easily fall into a trap of trying to do everything ourselves. While you can still be successful with this philosophy, you will always be limited by your own experience, skills, and perspective. As a practice owner, this can mean hiring and giving appropriate autonomy to a practice manager or partner. As an associate, this can mean realizing just because you learned something a certain way in school doesn't mean that's the only right way to do it.

2. Take calculated risks. Talk to any successful business owner and they will more often than not attribute the ability to accept calculated risks as a factor in their success. As a new graduate, this can mean stepping into a leadership position in practice, researching and attempting a surgical procedure for the first time, or being willing to take that pro-sal compensation package instead of resting in the security, and limitations, of a base salary.

3. Never settle for "good enough." Whether as a practice owner, associate, or support staff member, it's tempting to fall into the trap of going through the motion because you're doing "good enough" to treat your patients, lead your team, and take home a paycheck. There are several risks to doing this, though. Look back just a few years ago when we saw a string of layoffs in veterinary medicine because associates had been working for so long for their salary that they'd never paused to consider what value they were actually bringing to the practice. Any veterinarian can spay or neuter and we should always be looking for ways to make ourselves irreplaceable.

As a veterinary professional, the opportunities available are bountiful. Even though there are hurdles (student debt, the job market, etc.), using the advice offered in this book can help you learn from the mistakes and successes of your peers to pave your own way.

Stith Keiser was born in 1984 in Cheyenne, Wyoming, received a BA in Business Management from Hope College in 2007, and is currently the Manager of Career Development and My Veterinary Career for the American Animal Hospital Association. My Veterinary Career, founded by Stith upon graduation, is a veterinary matchmaking firm matching veterinarians and practice managers, at no charge, with all types and sizes of practices across North America. Stith's industry experience includes facilitating workshops and speaking at national and local veterinary conferences. He also writes for industry publications and websites. Additionally, Stith conducts career development-related workshops for student clubs and organizations at veterinary schools across the country. Stith is a member of VetPartners, Chair of the Career Development Special Interest Group, which most recently released the VetPartners/NVBMA/AAHA Mentorship Toolkit, and he serves on the American Animal Hospital Association's Recent Graduate Task Force.

In addition to his work with AAHA, Stith is also a partner in several companion animal and mixed animal practices.

Scott Keller

learned that animal care is more client oriented than animal oriented. No one tells you this in school, so we graduate with unreal expectations of how we can care for animals. Knowing this now, my advice centers around two principles and neither of them has to do with animal medicine.

First, people have different personalities. None are inherently good or bad, just different. They typically can be described by four categories. There are several resources that go into details about each personality type and you should study these. When I studied these personality types and determined early on in a conversation what personality type the client was, I would focus my approach to become more relatable to their personality type. Sounds odd to size someone up and then change what you do to accommodate his or her personality type, but after I started using this approach, frustrating clients and owner compliance really improved. I started to enjoy practice more because I could treat animals better when owners were more willing to opt for better treatment. Never pre-determine what you think owners want, but do determine what type of personality they have. When I started doing this, people were more agreeable.

Perhaps you will learn this before I did and save yourself years of frustration. Most of us get into veterinary medicine because we love animals, but it's really a people business. Veterinary medicine is as much about the human animal as it is about any other species. The sooner you realize this, the less frustration there will be. As a small animal practitioner, I was much less frustrated after I

Second, while in school you may do some role playing regarding different clients and situations, but you are never ready for any of them until you have self-confidence. College prepared me well for diagnosing, prescribing, and doing surgery. However, I initially lacked confidence when dealing with people. What if they asked me something I didn't know? What if I couldn't figure out what the problem was? These came to mind before I entered every exam room to speak with clients, and this made me uncomfortable in front of them.

This monkey was finally lifted off my back when I realized clients really don't need you to know everything, they need you to care enough to find out. The old axium, "Clients don't care how much you know until they know how much you care," is very true. So, never feel bad about not knowing something. Tell the client that you don't know, but will find out. Rely on colleagues, books, CE meetings, journals, and quality Internet resources to find out what you don't know. Share with your client what you now know and they will love you for taking time to care enough to find out answers.

Dr. R. Scott Keller was born in central Illinois in 1962. He was the son of a high school biology teacher who seemed to be the person to whom students brought injured wildlife. His father would bring them home and Scott would try nursing them back to health. That is where animal care started for him.

Dr. Keller earned his DVM from the University of Illinois in 1987. For the next 12 years, he worked in a small animal practice in a suburb of Chicago. In 1999, Dr. Keller left private practice to start the veterinary medical technology program at Joilet Junior College. Dr. Keller's interest in organized veterinary medicine has allowed him to serve as an officer in his regional veterinary medical association as a board member of his state veterinary medical association, and as a board member and president of the International Association of Veterinary Technician Educators.

Michele Laughlin

You will, undoubtedly, receive many words of wisdom, advice, and suggestions when you become a Veterinary Technician. You will be told the best way to place an IV catheter, the most effective way to restrain a fractious cat, or how to get Betadine stains out of your favorite scrubs. More than likely, you will be overwhelmed with a feeling of "now what?" What you may not receive is advice on what to do with an emotional client, a crying child, an angry co-worker, or your own burnout. These are things you will encounter every day!

The things that have stuck with me the most in my 25 years in the veterinary field really have nothing to do with the technical aspect of the job. Yes, the technical aspect of the job is critical. You have to know what you are doing, be comfortable in your position, and be okay with asking for help or asking questions. But you also have to know that there are many emotional, non-technical aspects to this job.

- Join your state technician association and utilize it. Volunteer in an area that interests you.
- Join NAVTA and utilize it.
- It's not just puppies and kittens. It's illness, injury, fractious, and feral. Be realistic.
- There are people attached to that leash, carrier, lead rope, and cage. Accept that you will deal with real, live people every day. Even if you aren't a "people person."
- Breathe. You will hit that vein, set that catheter, get that radiograph, and comfort that client. Just breathe.
- You're not perfect, but always strive to be the best you can be.
- Listen to your gut instinct.
- Listen to those with more knowledge and experience than you; you may just learn something. Someday, it will be you that is more knowledgeable and has more experience and you will become the teacher.
- Find a mentor.
- Be open to new ideas, but also know that some of the old, proven ones still work today.
- Speak up and be heard. Participate in your career. Be proactive, be active.
- Take your CE seriously. Don't just take CE classes to fulfill your requirements. Learn from them.
- Never stop learning.
- Volunteer.
- Network, network, network.
- Be professional... all the time!! It's a small world. Word of your behavior gets out quickly!
- Be a team player.
- Be cognizant of social media... the good, the bad, and the ugly of it.
- Take care of yourself physically and mentally.
- Be open to the career choices outside of being a clinical technician.
- Ask for help, offer help.
- You are not above doing laundry, cleaning kennels, mucking stalls, stocking rooms. It doesn't matter if you are a brand new technician or a seasoned one... stuff has to get done.
- Respect your clinic's receptionists. They are the lifeline of your clinic and their job is MUCH harder than you think.
- Respect your clinic's money... don't waste resources.
- "Dr. Google" will make your job challenging. Clients tend to believe everything they read on the Internet or hear from a breeder, groomer, or trainer. Educate them with the facts.
- There will be blood, sweat, tears, urine, feces, anal glands, reflux, biting, scratching, and kicking. Be prepared.
- Enjoy every day and soak it all in.

Michele E. Laughlin, AAS, CVT, is a Colorado native, born in 1960 and raised in Boulder. She has been married to her husband, Michael, for 35 years and she has two children, two grandsons, four grand-dogs, three dogs, three cats, and an old retired thoroughbred. Prior to her first veterinary receptionist job, she worked in the human medicine field doing data entry and also worked various retail jobs.
Michele has 25 years of experience in the veterinary field: 18 years in office management, hospital administration, client services supervision, and as a veterinary assistant. Clinic work includes mixed animal practice, 24-hour emergency care, and general practice. With seven years as a Certified Veterinary Technician, she has taken on a lead technician role, performed inventory, and worked in customer service. She served for three years on the board of the Colorado Association of Certified Veterinary Technicians (President-Elect, President, and Immediate Past President). Michele serves as an AVMA CVTEA Site Team Visit member (as needed) and is a member of CACVT and NAVTA.

Julie Legred USA

1. Do everything you can to learn and practice skills during your time in school and enhance and expand your knowledge and communication skills after you graduate.

In school, there is so much you have to learn. You don't have just one species to learn about, you have many. You not only have to learn nursing skills, but dentistry, radiology, laboratory testing, surgery, behavior, anesthesia, grief counseling, reproductive expertise, nutritional counseling, rehabilitation techniques, how to be an educator, and so on. There is so much you have to fit into two to four years. You definitely have to be ready for the challenge and believe in yourself. You will need to listen to your instructors, take advantage of every opportunity to ask questions, practice hands-on skills at every chance possible, and STUDY!

Take the time to learn about every species and all areas available to practice, because even though you may think you want to focus in one area of veterinary medicine, the more you learn and the more exposure you get to other areas, you may find an underlying passion in something else. You

never know what may be in your future years down the road. I grew up in a large city, wondered why my instructors were forcing me to learn about large animals, because I swore I was only going to be working with small animals. Ten years after graduating, I got married, moved to a very small town, and now am co-owners with my husband of a 200,000-pig swine genetics company. You just never know where you're going to end up or what opportunity will come your way!

One of the most difficult things you do on a day-to-day basis is to communicate. Many folks tend to be introverts in this profession, which means you don't get enough of the much-needed practice or guidance in communicating. You use your communication skills to talk to and educate clients; talk and interact with your veterinary healthcare team members; and communicate with labs, industry representatives, and so forth. By learning everything you can and understanding everything you learn, you gain the knowledge you need to speak with clients about everything they need to know to take care of their animals. You need to know what you are talking about to gain trust with clients, but also to be viewed as true professionals and an extremely important part of the veterinary healthcare team.

2. Support your state and national professional organizations.

You don't typically make tons of money as veterinary technicians - especially right out of school - so you have to be very cautious with your money. I promise that if you invest in the very minimal fees for professional memberships every year, you will not be sorry.

Shortly after I graduated as a technician, I became a single mom and worked three jobs trying to make ends meet with daycare costs and regular bills. It was a continuous struggle, but despite living paycheck to paycheck, there were two things that I made sure I saved money for every year: my Minnesota Association of Veterinary Technicians

(MAVT) membership and my NAVTA membership. I have been a member of both organizations since 1984. WOW! I'm really dating myself, but it is something I am very proud of and feel very strongly about.

For the longest time, I just paid my membership fee every year, looking forward to the MAVT newsletters, the discounted convention rates, the NAVTA Journals. I really thought that was why I became a member of both of these associations, not to mention that it looked good on my resume. I was asked by a friend of mine a few years into my career to help with an MAVT event and, soon after that, I found myself volunteering in various roles for MAVT and eventually went on to volunteer in various roles within NAVTA. I found that by actively participating, I felt I was giving back to my profession. At the same time, I was meeting so many different people and learning so much.

One of the biggest things I have learned through-out the years is that we are all involved in our professional organizations from day one just by becoming a member. Many people think that you have to become a board member or chairperson or committee member. They think that you only become a member for the "stuff" (journals, news-letters, website access, etc.) and yes, all of this is part of membership, but actually you are doing much more than you know! You are giving back to your profession and supporting it hugely by paying that membership fee every year. Just that small amount gives that much more money toward projects and initiatives, toward keeping fees down for you and all technicians, and toward covering journal costs and convention costs - all important in keeping our profession moving forward.

All technicians becoming one creates a bigger voice for us. With increased membership numbers, it shows our strength and professionalism. The rest of the veterinary industry only sees us as players and professionals by the numbers we bring. Increasing membership increases our awareness to these various industry representatives, potential sponsors, and partners, as well as to our allied associations. They see strength in numbers, which allows them to consider partnering and supporting projects and initiatives we are working on or want to pursue.

Membership gives you the voice that you deserve and allows you to weigh in on what direction you want your profession to go. There are so many opportunities out there today and, many times, the only way you know they are there is through professional organizations and networking. Be proud of your profession, support it and let your voice be heard!

3. Networking will be your vital link!
You should be thrilled to death that you are graduating and that you are well on your way to the best career EVER! You will find a position as a veterinary technician, making this a very exciting time. Please remember to keep it that way. Always enjoy and be happy in your position. If, for some reason, you find you aren't enjoying what you're doing, don't feel like you are failing. There are many positions for us in many different capacities. If you accept a position and are not happy in it, then change it! It is almost a given that at some point in your career, you will experience some level of burnout, so it is important to realize the next steps.

Sometimes, it may be as simple as focusing in a certain area of the hospital and becoming the "expert" on that subject, or maybe even consider specializing in a specific area without leaving the practice you are in. Sometimes just finding a passion to focus on can be enough. Other times, the hospital you are in might not be the right fit. Different personalities, beliefs, or ways of utilizing technicians can make it very hard to enjoy what you are doing. Don't settle! Know that there are many practices that will allow you to grow and fully support and utilize your skills, because they know how effective you can be as a technician and how you can truly have a very positive effect on the practice. Being proactive in finding your dream job and focusing on your passion is a good thing, even if you are happy in your current position. Networking will keep you in the loop of what is out there. It will open up doors for you in your passion areas. Keep your opportunities at your fingertips. You can't expect to have the opportunities there when you need them, at the drop of your hat. You need to build relationships to reach some of these goals. Attend conferences and talk to speakers, sales reps, leaders in veterinary medicine. Don't be afraid to step out of your comfort zone - do anything to meet people in the area of what makes you happy. You never know what may come up and the more you put yourself out there, the more your name will come to mind for others. Opportunities will arise without you even realizing or expecting it. The sky is the limit, and nothing is impossible!

Always be happy. Life is too short, so you need to enjoy what you do. This is the best career and there are so many possibilities out there. The veterinary field is changing all the time, and if it isn't there right now, don't think it isn't possible, because there are many individuals out there in our profession who have taken their knowledge and passion to make it into something that can make them money, keep them happy, allow them to enjoy what they do, and stay in this great profession for many years to come!

Julie Legred, CVT, graduated from the University of Minnesota - Waseca in June, 1985, with an Associate's degree in Applied Science in Animal Health Technology. That same month, she passed both the Minnesota State and Veterinary Technician National Exam and earned the credential of Certified Veterinary Technician.

Julie has worked in many areas of veterinary technology, including small animal and exotic practices, research, education (instructor and program director), swine genetics, corporate medicine, leadership, management, and consulting.

She currently holds the position of Executive Director of the National Association of Veterinary Technicians in America (NAVTA), Senior Manager of Veterinary Technician Programs for NAVC, and also works with her husband in their swine genetics business, LSG Healthsystems, as Special Projects Coordinator.

Julie has been very active in professional organizations, working with the Minnesota Association of Veterinary Technicians for the past 17 years, and on the board of NAVTA as a Member-at-Large and as President (2008 and 2011). She was on the American Veterinary Medical Association's (AVMA) Committee on Veterinary Technician Education and Activities (CVTEA) since 2005 and served on the AVMA's Convention Management and Planning Committee from 2007 to 2013. Currently, she is on their Task Force for Continuing Education. Finally, Julie has held the veterinary technician board position on the Companion Animal Parasite Council since 2009.

Julie speaks and writes on various topics, including parasitology, leadership, career opportunities within veterinary technology, and more. She has fun talking to kids about animal health care and dog bite prevention. In 2005 and 2007, Julie was awarded the Minnesota Veterinary Technician of the Year Award.

David Liss USA

Technical skills can be learned, people skills are much harder to assimilate, especially for the introvert. It's said that greater than 75% of those in the veterinary profession are introverted and a significant portion of us feel under-paid, if not outright under-valued. Those who claim job and wage satisfaction aren't necessarily solely the extroverts. Who are they? They are skilled negotiators, introverts and extroverts alike.

Negotiation skills are useful in all areas of life and imperative in some, like salary and benefit negotiation. Looking for a new job or already employed but want a raise? Here are some tips I wish I'd known when I started:

- *Do your research.* Know what an adequate income is for your level of training and the responsibility you'll be taking on. Look at salary.com, glassdoor.com, and the Bureau of Labor Statistics for information about your specific locale.

- *Know what you want and what you have to offer.* Have you found a way to retain revenue for your hospital? Don't be afraid to talk about how you've impacted client retention or increased new client revenue. Negotiation is about mutually positive outcomes, each of you must have something the other wants. What makes you a valuable asset to your hospital?

- *Direct and open communication is a key strategy.* Ask your manager or supervisor what you can do to ensure the maximum amount possible at your review. Then check in throughout the year to make sure you are fulfilling those requirements. Ask what a realistic expectation is for that raise. No one's going to walk away happy if you're thinking of a $5 per hour increase and that's outside your hospital's budget.

- *Practice.* No, seriously, practice. Call an insurance company and ask for a quote(you might even save money), go to a coffee shop and ask for a glass of ice water and don't order anything else, negotiate with your roommate about taking over a chore you don't want to do, ask the cashier to give you change in $1s or quarters, or ask the manager at your local grocery store to carry an item you want but they don't have. There are daily opportunities for negotiation, don't let them slip away. They mean better pay later, when negotiation really matters.

Remember that negotiation is not a competition, it's a collaboration and teamwork is the cornerstone of quality veterinary care.

David Liss was born in 1985. In 2007 he graduated from Occidental College in Los Angeles with a BA in Sociology and became a licensed RVT. He is now a double board-certified veterinary technician specialist in emergency/critical care and small animal internal medicine and has diverse background in emergency and critical care nursing. He has been technician manager at two different 24-hour referral/specialty facilities in the Los Angeles area, has contributed to numerous veterinary textbooks and was awarded the

Veterinary Technician Educator of the Year award in 2012 by the Western Veterinary Conference. David currently directs the veterinary technology program at Platt College in Los Angeles, works as an ICU technician at VCA Veterinary Specialists of the Valley in Woodland Hills, California, runs his own consulting business, Veterinary Training and Consulting, Inc., and lectures worldwide.

Margreet Lockhorst   The Netherlands

In 2009, I participated in VetCoach as a veterinarian. For this edition of VetTeamCoach, I reflect on my work as Chef de Clinique, veterinary manager, and member of the veterinary disciplinary board. During my career as a veterinarian, I have worked in many different types of practices, varying from a one-vet small animal practice in a little sleeping village to a big emergency clinic in the city of Amsterdam. These are totally different worlds. In the one-vet practice, you are practically on your own; you may have the help of one or two veterinary assistants, or sometimes only the wife of the practice owner. Clients will often make remarks, such as, "Where is our own vet?" or "Where is the real doctor?" It can feel like a very lonely world without any inter-collegial veterinarian contact. In a big clinic, you can encounter vets in many

stages of their careers: specialists, veterinary nurses, managers, chef de clinique, and directors. Here you never feel alone, but you also never feel like your own boss. It so happened that I became head of staff in this big emergency clinic. It happened by accident, it was never my intention. It started because I got irritated about how the daily work was (not) organized, and I started to make work schedules for the vets and nurses. If I had known at that time what organizing and running a big clinic meant, I might not have rushed in. A veterinarian is not necessarily trained as a manager, but you can learn.

If you are in a leading position, you are not "one of the guys" anymore. Staff treats you differently and they become selective in the things they tell you. The same thing happened to one of the nurses. I changed her position in making her head nurse, and within days she felt left out. If you want to avoid this, it is better to hire someone from outside the clinic as a manager.

Staff meetings need to be held on a regular basis. You need an agenda; staff can add issues in advance, and you always have a survey at the end. And this is another issue I want to share with you. You hear things on the floor, you know in advance some people have issues, but during the survey at the staff meeting everyone is silent. Don't think all the problems are resolved! They just don't want, or don't dare, to share it with you or the group. If you are aware of this, you can try to help by asking open questions, talk to staff members in smaller groups or one on one.

I had to deal with approximately 40 people. Some people draw a lot of attention while others were almost forgotten because they never give you any trouble. There's another pitfall that was pointed out to me by a dear friend from a totally different profession (architecture). He asked me over dinner, when I was telling him about all my experiences: "Why do you spend so much time and energy over people without the skills, correct attitude, and great personality instead of people who are worth investing in?" This was a real eye-opener and after I realized this, dealing with staff became more appealing to me.

For the last three years, I have been a member of the Dutch National Veterinary Disciplinary Board. For a veterinarian or nurse accused of wrongdoing, it is a very stressful event if you have to deal with a case against you. If clients complain to you or members of the staff about the treatment of their pet, please be very direct in your communication. This means making a quick response, offering a meeting, and being open if a mistake has taken place. And do not present the invoice at the same time. In my experience, it is not a good idea to let the communication with the complaining client be handled by the clinic manager. The client wants to communicate with the vet or nurse who participated in the treatment of their pet. The clinic manager can be supportive to the vet or nurse in preparing for the meeting with the complaining client. In those cases where the client still wants to present the case to the disciplinary board, it is important that the manager (or owner of the clinic) is present at the hearing to support their staff member.

Dr. Margreet Lockhorst was born in The Hague, The Netherlands, in 1962. She studied Veterinary Medicine and graduated from the Utrecht University in The Netherlands in 1992.

While waiting on admission to vet school, Dr. Lockhorst became an operating room nurse, and worked in a Rotterdam University (human) hospital from 1982 to 1985. After graduation from vet school in 1992, Margreet worked in a small animal clinic and as horse event veterinarian for equine endurance competitions (FEI). From 1993 to 1996, she worked in the first veterinary emergency clinic in Amsterdam, and after that studied as a specialist trainee in equine internal medicine at the University of Utrecht (1996 to 1997).

Margreet moved back to Amsterdam as Chef de Clinique for the emergency clinic in Amsterdam (1997 to 1998) and then as Managing Director from1999 to 2000. Since 2001, she has been the veterinary manager at a small animal clinic in Eersel, The Netherlands, and also serves as a member of the Veterinary Disciplinary Board.

Linda Markland

Communication

Veterinary Medicine: the branch of science that deals with prevention, diagnosis, and treatment of disease, disorder, and injury of animals. Nowhere in that description does it mention dealing with PEOPLE!

When I first entered veterinary medicine, nearly 40 years ago, I had completed all the prerequisites for human nursing, then I decided to change to veterinary medicine so I could help animals and not work with people. Of course, it didn't take me long to realize that people are the reason we see most animals. Animals do not bring themselves to the veterinary hospital, people do. People make the decisions on how far we can go to treat their pets. People pay the bills.

Learning to communicate with people - your clients and your team - is one of the most important skills you can learn. Remember, they are the reason your paycheck doesn't bounce!
Thinking that you can work only with animals and not with the humans attached to those animals is quite unrealistic. Whether you are working in the kennel, as a technician in the back, or even as deep into the practice as the surgery technician,

you WILL have to talk with the pet owner, giving them a progress report on their pet's condition, etc. Even if, by some miracle, you never or rarely have to talk to a client, you will have to communicate with your team. People!
Do not make the mistake I did by thinking you are choosing a profession where you do not have to deal with people. Veterinary Medicine is a PEOPLE profession. It is a relationship-building profession. PEOPLE, PEOPLE, PEOPLE!

Empowerment

One of the most important things I did in my career was to find a veterinarian who not only allowed me, but encouraged me, to grow in my profession. As an RVT, I was allowed to do all we are legally allowed to do. If I was uncomfortable in the task, not as proficient as I could be, my veterinarian took the time to show me and then empower me to learn more and do more.
I accompanied him to most veterinary meetings: radiology, pathology, surgery, local associations, and more. At first, I was the only technician allowed, but when the attendees saw that I was professional and could contribute to the discussions - and believe me, it took me many meetings to gain the courage to do this - others started bringing their technicians to the meetings. This was a wonderful opportunity for me to hear what my boss was hearing, and it gave us many things to discuss concerning various cases when we returned to the practice.

I hear many technicians complain that they work in a situation where they are not allowed to practice their skills and grow in the practice or their career, or are not shown respect. I say why are you still there? There are many veterinarians looking for qualified technicians to help them practice the best medicine and grow their practice. Look for these opportunities, and don't take no for an answer if you really want to work at a specific location. There are too many opportunities for technicians for you to stay somewhere you are not happy and fulfilled.

If the position you want is not available where you are, either try to develop it - sometimes if you take the initiative, others will follow - or move on.
The only thing limiting you is your imagination. Life is too short and your career is too important to settle or be unhappy.

Enrichment
When I first started working in veterinary medicine as a kennel attendant and then as a veterinary assistant, I thought I was the only one experiencing the challenges, frustrations, and fears that we all face in our profession. Then I was invited to help organize a technician association in our community. I learned I was not the Lone Ranger and many more people were experiencing the same challenges.

Do you want to make a difference in your profession? Get involved! Through local, state, and national associations, you can make a difference, both for yourself and for future veterinary technicians. Start by looking for opportunities to help facilitate changes in your work environment. It can be a small change, such as becoming the nutrition educator for both your clients and your team. Set up and organize how it will work in your practice. You have just become a leader. Next, become a member of your local technician association. If there is not one, help start one. Hopefully, your employer will pay your dues. Next, join a committee, something of interest to you. The advantages of becoming involved in your associations are many and vary with the individual.

When I became involved in our local technician association, I met others who were experiencing similar challenges. I also learned new procedures to be used in the hospital and opportunities within my community and beyond. I began networking, which has enhanced my career beyond my expectations. Our profession needs dedicated and passionate individuals to help improve and grow our influence.

Leadership
When I first began my career in veterinary medicine, I listened to and watched everyone around me so I could learn as fast as possible and become an

asset, not a liability to the practice. During those tentative first days, weeks, months, and even years, I was very impressionable. I found myself gravitating toward the more professional-acting members of our team and distancing myself from those less productive and professional, hoping to learn and earn the respect of those I respected.

I knew I was watching them, but I did not know they were watching me. As I learned from them, asking questions and asking to learn more, they were making plans to promote me from kennel assistant to veterinary assistant to head surgical nurse and training supervisor. This all happened in the span of one year. Four years later, I was asked to enroll in the Animal Health Technician Program at our local college because a visiting veterinarian that I worked with, the Program Director, was impressed by my skill and passion. I went on to teach in that program after I graduated.
I tell you this, not to impress but to enlighten you on the fact that you are being watched whether you realize it or not, and you don't know who is watching.

This hit home with me many times, but at the Western Veterinary Conference a couple of years ago a technician approached me and was in tears. I asked her what was wrong, but she said it's what is right that brings these tears. She was ready to leave our profession, which she loved but could not advance where she was, and didn't think it would be better elsewhere. She had heard me speak on career opportunities and that your imagination is your only limiting factor, and she was inspired. She had ideas, but didn't have the courage to try until she heard me. Wow! I told her that I had no idea that my little speech would make such a difference. She said it wasn't only the words but the passion and excitement with which I said these words. I could give you many stories about unknowingly influencing people by what I have said and done. I have no idea how many others who didn't tell me are out there. Remember, you are being watched by friends, family, and strangers and you may never know how you influenced them. Please set a good example!

Linda Markland, RVT, currently works for VPI as a Veterinary Relations Specialist and is located in Peoria, Arizona. She graduated from Orange Coast College in Costa Mesa, California, in 1982. Also, she is a WVC Technician Education Manager.

Linda has been involved with the veterinary profession for more than 30 years. Her experiences are extremely diverse and broad, ranging from small animal clinical practice to corporate and educational positions, with a special interest in practice management.

In her spare time, Linda represents Orange County on the California Veterinary Medical Association Registered Veterinary Technician Committee, and is past Chair of this committee. She is a member of many local, regional, and state veterinary associations, serving these organizations in many different capacities. She is also a member of VetPartners, where she serves on the Program Committee and the Ethics Committee, as well as on the Industry Task Force.

Linda has spoken at the Wild West Veterinary Conference on practice management topics. She is also a moderator at all of the major conferences. In 2012, she won the CVMA Outstanding RVT in Non Private Practice. Thereafter, the Board of Governors re-named the award the Linda Markland Award.

Pam Maurer 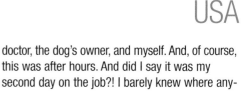 USA

1. Help Found in the Strangest Places

The second day on the job at a new practice in a new town, I found myself staring at a St. Bernard caesarean section. The dog was massive, taking three people to lift her onto the surgery table; the doctor, the dog's owner, and myself. And, of course, this was after hours. And did I say it was my second day on the job?! I barely knew where anything was located! I hadn't run anesthesia in several months as I recently moved and was job searching. How else to learn, other than to dive right in? The doctor I was working with was very supportive, helping me to set up surgery, get the dog all prepped, making sure my nerves weren't getting the best of me. The biggest surprise and help was from the St. Bernard's owner. You see, she was an RN. She knew it was my second day on the job, and probably recognized the state of my nerves. And dared to ask if she could help! With anything! Well, she became a bit of a gopher and a bit of moral support for me along the way. Asking little questions that really helped a lot, and kept me focused. The St. Bernard did well. And the pups did well also. And that RN? Susan became a great client friend to me. I was always her Go-To person.

This story is about realizing where help may appear, and learning all you can from that instantaneous helping angel. And to not discount the unorthodox help. Some would say, "Don't trust a client to help! They don't know what they're doing!" In equine medicine, when out on house calls, sometimes the only help is the client. They know their horse. Most often, they know the quirks to restrain their horse. These knowledgeable people help to keep a situation under control and safe for everyone. Or, how do you think your dental hygienist (or other human practitioner) feels when you start talking their talk, understanding everything, and asking questions most patients don't consider? They are either flabbergasted or they begin to talk even more! It is surprising the things you can glean from clients, drug reps, and fellow colleagues when you open up and start to listen. It's all about assessing the moment, using the hands and minds at your disposal to the best possible advantage, keeping in mind the safety of patient/client/staff, and practicing medicine within the confines of the law.

2. Burnout and Compassion Fatigue

Two weeks before Christmas many years ago, I started to get massive headaches, nearly migraine level. Never before had I experienced something so awful, so pervasive, and so debilitating. I worked, but felt severely out of sorts. The headaches got to the point where my doctor ordered me to go to the emergency room right then and there to get a CT scan. Up to this point, we had tried many different drugs, from high dose anti-inflammatories, to migraine meds, to even a cocktail of caffeine, acetaminophen, and valium. Nothing worked. The CT was clear, no tumors. The emergency room doctor told me that my headaches were because of the holidays. Talking out loud, my doctor was thinking to pass me along to a specialist or, hey, let's try physical therapy. Several months later, wow, what a change. My headaches had a name. Tension headaches. Yeah, that would fit veterinary medicine. So, I learned through physical therapy how to be even more cognizant of how my body functions and the tell-tail signs of a tension headache, and what to do about it.

I didn't realize for many years after my headache dilemma, that I was on the downward spiral of burnout and, also, compassion fatigue. Initially, I thought that I was spending too much time reading and researching information for work. After moving down a different path, I was able to look from the outside in, realizing the underlying cause of my headaches. The loss of my National Show Horse mare removed me from my ability to take time away from work and do something fun. I'll always have animals, but that doesn't mean I'm always at work just to be around animals. I forgot to take the time to take care of myself. To take more than just a couple days off every few months. That I needed to have a real vacation, leaving work behind, and doing something entirely different.

After realizing how all the pieces fit into place that contributed to my burnout, I started to hear the topic of compassion fatigue being discussed. At first, it all sounded like a bunch of warm and fuzzy psychobabble. But then I decided to read a short article about it. I was dumbfounded. I recognized a few signs in myself. No wonder I was finding it harder and harder to connect with many things going on at the hospital. I was having a problem caring about my environment. Don't get me wrong, I loved working in the hospital, I loved my patients, my coworkers were great. But I had worn myself down enough that I did not know how to pick myself up from rock bottom. I would move on to try something new, never properly dealing with what was affecting me. Compassion fatigue has been recognized in human nurses for more than 50 years, but only in the last hand full of years is veterinary medicine coming to recognize that technicians and others can easily suffer from compassion fatigue as well.

If I had understood burnout and compassion fatigue sooner, I might still be a practicing credentialed technician working in a hospital. Instead, I now focus more on the people development side of business.

3. Lifelong Learning

We work in an industry that screams with the need for lifelong learning. With the ever advancing and changing medical practices, drug laws, and licensing regulations, to name a few, there is always something to learn. After high school, I attended a university and community college for a few years. I disliked school, those two years of ridiculous repeat courses from high school. It wasn't until I discovered veterinary medicine and graduated from tech school that I really caught the learning bug.

After being an RVT for a few years, I got a bit bored. I tend to do that. Conquer what I'm doing (ha ha! It took me a few more years to learn that one can never conquer being an RVT), then seek something else to do. So, then I finished my bachelor's degree and changed jobs a couple of times trying to find my niche. Then I got the learning bug again, and started my MBA. I disliked my job and decided to go back to school again full time, while the economy figured itself out, to work on a second master's degree. This time, it was more than an academic education I signed up for; it was also a cultural one. I moved to England. Tea, anyone?

Along the way, I've begun to figure out who I am. Lifelong learning is not just about learning about new drugs, procedures, or policies. It's also learning about yourself, where your strengths and weak-nesses lie, and what really lights your learning fire. For me, I'm figuring out I like helping others. I seem to have a natural talent for coaching and mentoring. I'm still interested in the medicine, but I'd rather help people to get the most out of their career in veterinary medicine. What do they need? How can I help? That is part of my new journey.

What is your new journey? How do you want to get there? There are tons of topics that are relevant to veterinary medicine. One that seems fairly new that peaks my interest is veterinary forensics. What about the VTS credentials? What a great way to deepen your knowledge, skills, and abilities to provide top notch nursing care for your animal patients. What about learning more about adult education, business, human resources, accounting, or better yet, public health? There are many more options out there. Build your network of colleagues that will help you grow your interests.

4. Mentoring
I never realized until years later that the people who helped me out, who were my sounding boards, also were my mentors. I wish I understood and realized sooner in my career the importance of finding mentors, thereby removing the need to make drastic career changes. And I say mentors plural for a reason. As we all know, each person is different, and with those differences comes a different way of looking at each situation. Some are good at looking at the whole picture of your career; others, at minute instances during a particular workday. Some are good listeners. My mentors have been those outside of my immediate work environment, and not all have been long-term mentors. Many have been a one-time meeting. They were able to provide unbiased observations and questions, helping me to delve deeper into what I was having problems with, or just trying to understand how best to make a decision.

Mentors can be anyone you feel will help you. Sometimes it's just a conversation over coffee to discuss a situation. Your ability to appropriately use that conversation to improve and/or better your life and career is what makes it valuable. Time is never wasted during these conversations. Or, you approach someone you feel can really help you grow your career. Maybe this person has traveled a path you are interested in, and then you approach them with a key purpose: to learn and understand their successes and failures. The important point to remember when having mentors is to use everyone's time wisely. Do not expect them to set the conversation; you have to come prepared with what you are seeking help for. Only then is the mentor truly able to help you advance your career by providing advice and encouragement.

Another important point to realize about mentoring is that mentors will come and go, but the friend-ships made will be everlasting. The variety and frequency of my mentors over the years has spanned many generations, but also many industries outside of veterinary medicine. I've had mentors that have been both domestically and internationally located in education, human nursing, sales and marketing, human resources, learning and development, leadership development, and business development, to name a few. There's a multitude to learn from the world that is found outside of veterinary medicine that is very much applicable to veterinary medicine. The path I took was very much based upon who I am as a person; my behaviors, my traits, my personality, and my interests. I followed my instincts. Are you following yours?

Pam Maurer, CVT, was born on a U.S. Marine base on Okinawa, Japan while her dad was in the U.S. Air Force. After her family left Okinawa, they moved to two more bases in New Mexico and Florida. Pam's dad retired from military service, and her parents moved the family back to California, where she grew up in Silicon Valley.

Pam discovered veterinary medicine during the late 1990s after her National Show Horse mare required surgery due to colic. While volunteering at the equine surgical/referral facility, Pam attended the veterinary technology program at Foothill College, graduating and becoming licensed in 2001. Pam's veterinary experience has been in general practice, research, ECC/specialty, equine, and pharmaceutical outside sales.

Although Pam has had a broad view of veterinary medicine, she has really enjoyed being a team leader and mentor the most. Her education has demonstrated her interest in business and people leadership by completing a BA degree from St. Petersburg College in Veterinary Hospital Management, an MBA with a concentration in Leadership from Walden University, and an MSc from Northumbria University (UK) in International Human Resource Management.

While Pam was working and going to school full time, she worked alongside a small team to launch the California Registered Veterinary Technicians Association, where she was president for two non-consecutive terms. Pam currently chairs the mentor committee, developing a mentor program that rolled out a pilot study during the summer of 2013.

During Pam's free time, she likes to work on cross-stitch projects; the more complicated the project, the better. She also likes to read, play with her cat, spend time with her gelding, garden, and travel to the UK where her fiancé is finishing his PhD.

Marie McNamara   USA

The veterinary industry is no different than other industries when it comes to employees. Employees are any business's greatest asset. They can also be their biggest liability. Obviously, it is important to choose the right talent for your business. Placing equal emphasis on soft skills and hard or technical skills is critical to finding the right person for your team. To a degree, technique can be taught. Overall attitude and communications skills are much more difficult to teach or change in an employee. As an example, a veterinary assistant can be taught proper restraint techniques. It is much more difficult to teach how to communicate with difficult clients or co-workers.

On an employee's first day, it is important to teach them the practice's culture, operating standards, and appropriate behavior in relation to different work situations. Almost immediately, new employees will begin to pick up on personalities and behaviors of other employees. If a new employee is not taught what is acceptable, they will draw on what they have learned from past work experiences or employers rather than what is acceptable in your organization. Establish a set of guidelines on the more important issues that might arise - issues like how to deal with conflicting instructions, what to do when other employees are gossiping, how performance is rated and evaluations conducted, and what to do when another employee is violating a procedure or guideline are important to discuss. In doing so, new employees will understand what is expected of them. Follow up the initial orientation meeting with one or two subsequent meetings in the ensuing weeks to discuss any situations that have arisen and any areas that need clarification or further training. Other rules to live by:

1. Admit when you have done something wrong and take responsibility for it. Your co-workers will respect your integrity even in the face of a mistake. Promise to learn from it and do so.
2. Get all the facts before passing judgment. Often things are not what they seem and there are two sides to every story.
3. Avoid gossip at all costs. Gossip is anything that is not relevant to you or your position. Do not comment on another person's pay raise, what they wear or how they handle a client. Only involve yourself in those things that you are responsible for and can do something about.
4. Do not look the other way. Report problems or issues to the appropriate person. Making sure policy or standards are followed is good for the whole team. This ensures consistency so the team can operate as one.
5. Do establish and understand guidelines for performance. If you know what is expected of you or you set clear expectations for your team, everyone will have a clear understanding of acceptable behavior.

Marie Mondi McNamara, CVPM grew up in New Hartford, New York, and from a young age worked on and off for her father at his veterinary practice, New Hartford Animal Hospital. While in college, she became a full-time receptionist at the practice and over the years, worked her way through all of the positions there, becoming the hospital manager in 1993. As the animal hospital grew, she learned the financial side of running a business and became skilled in management, human resource, OSHA, inventory management, and marketing and advertising. In 1996, Marie completed Hollander's Management Program and spent the next year and a half rewriting hospital policy and the employee manual to reflect the practice's mission and vision. She retrained all the employees to share this vision. Tracking statistics became everyone's responsibility and what to do in the face of downward trends became a group effort. The employees were empowered to help grow the practice. Programs were developed and training seminars instituted to standardize what the practice was communicating to the clients and how the staff communicated with each other. Marie's efforts helped the hospital earn accreditations from the American Animal Hospital Association in 1997 and the New York State Veterinary Medical Society in 2003, accreditations they currently hold.

In 2001, Marie earned her certification as a Certified Veterinary Practice Manager. Over the past 12 years, she has mentored many less experienced managers, privately and through the Veterinary Hospital Manager's Association. Marie currently sits on the CVPM application review committee and the Veterinary Hospital Manager's Association Ethics committee. She earned her MBA in 2010.
Marie credits much of her overall success to her father and mentor, Dr. Frank A. Mondi. Through the years, she has had the privilege to work alongside someone she considers one of the greatest visionaries in her life. Marie lives in New Hartford, New York with her husband and three daughters.

Cynthia Medina

USA

While helping to educate veterinary technicians for the last 17 years, I have learned that the hardest thing to teach anyone is a solid set of "soft skills." Not your technical skills or occupational requirements, but your attitude and social graces.

Since soft skills are often the first thing to impact your employers' and team members' opinions of you, they will quickly earn you a "label" in the field - good or bad. Are you a slacker, drama queen, pest, bully, or doormat, or are you a problem solver, top performer, motivator, go-getter, or star employee? If you don't fall in the positive grouping, then it is likely that your soft skills need some substantial improvement.

Growing these non-technical abilities, presenting them clearly during interviews, and utilizing them consistently with your teammates will highly impact your salary, job progression, career options, and value in the eyes of your employers.
35 Essential Soft Skills:

1) Adaptability - Able to learn, able to be taught, curious, flexible/not intimated by change
2) Agreeability - Able to play well with others, pleasant, enjoyable, likable
3) Appearance - Well put together, looks the part of a medical professional, appeals to all clients - including the conservative ones
4) Communication - Sounds the part of a professional vet tech, polished in person/on the phone/online, enunciates, uses proper grammar, makes solid eye contact, has positive body language, able to listen
5) Confidence - Poised and polished, instills trust, has the skills to back it up
6) Conflict resolution - Directly communicates with the appropriate person away from clients' eyes/ears, effective complaints (not whining), respect for authority/the big picture, avoids gossip
7) Conscientious - Double checks important tasks, dedicated, learns from mistakes
8) Creative - Assesses effectiveness, finds new solutions to old problems, thinks quickly
9) Critical thinking - Problem solver, has common sense, aware of safety issues, attentive to the mood of others around you
10) Criticism & resulting growth - Able to accept criticism, able to change and develop as an employee, actively seeks feedback and asks questions
11) Emotion control - Doesn't take things personally, not moody, has solid personal boundaries
12) Emotional investment in your career - Cares, is passionate for the work, takes steps to avoid burnout or compassion fatigue
13) Etiquette & manners - Says please and thank you, courteous, nice handshake, doesn't step on team members' toes, appropriate physical interactions, appropriate social media postings
14) Gives credit where credit is due - Recognizes others' efforts, encourages teammates, doesn't steal ideas
15) Interactions with customers - Handles difficult or upset clients smoothly and calmly,

has a positive/happy approach, able to empathize, strong listener, grace in negative situations

16) **Integrity** - Dependable, consistent, trustworthy, respects confidentiality, ethical, non-judgmental

17) **Intuition** - Pays attention to gut instincts and reacts quickly and appropriately in urgent situations

18) **Leadership by example** - Shows leadership in any level position, shares control, is a "dream leader" but still intervenes and disciplines appropriately

19) **Managing diversity** - Respects and under-stands cultural and multi-generational differences, builds bridges through helping others, influences company culture positively

20) **Mentorship** - Builds up coworkers, courteous to trainees and interns, easily motivates others

21) **Negotiation & persuasion** - Able to influence others, enjoys educating clients and trainees

22) **Networking** - Builds support, keeps an eye on the future, understands the importance of community connections

23) **Office politics** - Knows the unspoken rules of the team, avoids supervisor/co-worker pet peeves

24) **Patience** - With self, others, cranky or nervous clients, nervous interns, uncooperative patients

25) **Personal accountability** - Takes responsibility for actions, apologizes when appropriate, assesses need for improvement

26) **Planning** - Avoids procrastination, has personal goals, understands role in the mission of the business

27) **Project management** - Goal setter, able to prioritize, meets/beats deadlines, acknowledges the contributions of team members

28) **Positive attitude & optimism** - Winner not whiner, stands out in a crowd, stays professional on bad days, smiles, laughs, has an appropriate sense of humor

29) **Resilience** - Able to move on from a past issue, bounces back, stays positive during the tough times

30) **Risk taking** - Takes on personal challenges, pushes beyond limits, speaks up

31) **The "selfs"** - Self-awareness, self-discipline, self-motivation, subtle self-promotion

32) **Stress management** - Handles pressure well, has self-control, acts instead of reacts, perseveres

33) **Teamwork** - Treats others well, contributes, helps others, looks for things to do, provides and seeks support

34) **Time management** - Multi-tasker, follows through, arrives at least 5 minutes early, categorizes tasks: immediate/do later/do tomorrow/etc.

35) **Work ethic** - Consistently exceeds employers' and team members' expectations

Want to advance in your career, gain more responsibility (and a better salary), and make a huge difference at every job you will ever have? It's easy - improve the quality of your charisma and you will go far!

Cynthia McNeil Medina has worked as a veterinary technician educator and administrator for 18 years as the Director of Student Services for Bel-Rea Institute in Denver, Colorado (www.belrea.edu). She is also the Director of Product and Development for Ready Vet - Emergency Response Plans and Training, providing comprehensive and customizable emergency/disaster planning for veterinary hospitals and training programs (www.readyvet.co).

While growing up in the San Francisco Bay Area, Cynthia was active in ballet, musical theater, and youth camps. After graduating Magna Cum Laude with a Bachelor of Arts in Psychology from Westmont College in Santa Barbara, California, in 1994, Cynthia went on to earn a Master of Arts in Counseling Psychology from the University of Denver in 1996. Following graduate school, Cynthia taught career courses at a community college and worked in private practice before discovering Bel-Rea. Cynthia actively performed and competed in ice dance and Irish dance in her 20s and 30s, but retired from the performing arts to spend more time with her three children and husband.

Cynthia is a positive and dynamic leader with expertise in the areas of emergency preparedness, non-profit consulting, faculty development, policy writing, and mediation. Known for her excellent public speaking, program development, and public relations skills, Cynthia has worked actively to increase the professional image and responsibility level of veterinary technicians in the field and to encourage a business-savvy approach among managers, directors, and veterinarians.

Sarah Meyer-Paterson   USA

Having a career in veterinary medicine/nursing and working with animals is a privilege, not a right. Handle them with respect, even when they are "aggressive." Chances are, these sentient beings are anxious and/or scared and deserve your patience and empathy. Pretend your patients are from a foreign land and do not speak your language. Everyone understands a pleasant tone of voice and a gentle touch.

Your patients' safety is #1. Be an advocate. If a co-worker is being unnecessarily rough, speak up in an assertive, but not aggressive, way. Say, "Let me help you. Cujo seems really nervous and I can see you are frustrated." Unfortunately, I have seen patient abuse and after witnessing it, I vowed it would NEVER happen again on my watch. If you feel a post-surgical patient needs additional analgesics (after assessing their parameters and anesthesia/surgical report, of course), speak up. I will always speak up on behalf of the animals in my charge and be mindful of my actions and those of my team members.

Compare your knowledge base from your first day of veterinary/technician school until now. A majority of clients have less than "first day" knowledge about how to properly care for their pets. Has a fearful client had a bad experience during a previous visit (a pet died after an ovariohysterectomy or perhaps a staff member was less than friendly and helpful)? This fear may be holding them back from asking questions and they will turn to less than credible sources for information.

It is our responsibility to educate them if we expect compliance and successful outcomes for our patients. Be empathetic and ask if they have questions/concerns - their reply may surprise you!

Ask questions. You don't know everything and you never will! It is quite disheartening to complete a task and be told you did it incorrectly. It is also frustrating to those around you to have to "fix" your mistake. We all prefer humble co-workers who acknowledge weaknesses, but are willing to improve to become more productive team members.

Lead by example. Do you constantly look at your phone or roll your eyes behind the manager's back? Someone will assume that behavior is inacceptable. If you find yourself getting frustrated with a co-worker's complacent work ethic, perhaps they learned it from you. Act professionally and you'll be surrounded by the like.

"Show them what you can do, don't tell them." After you get the job, it's up to you to prove your value through competent actions, not inflated words.

Make "cheat sheets" (laminated pocket-size card or a small binder) for metric conversions, formulas for calculating common fluid additives and drug dosages/concentrations, etc., for quick reference.

Earning your degree/license is only the first step to becoming a great doctor/nurse. You have the basics, but still have a lot to learn. Get more than the minimum annual CE hours required. Even if you are not licensed, if you are handling patients in any capacity, you need CE. Advancements are made in veterinary medicine every day - be part of the progression.

Sarah Meyer-Paterson, LVT, has been fortunate to travel from one coast to another and attributes her skill and success as a technician to the many great veterinary professionals she has met along the way. She started her career in the veterinary world as a kennel worker at a small animal practice, graduated from Lincoln Memorial University (Harrogate, Tennessee) and has been a Licensed Veterinary Technician since 2002. As a technician, Sarah has worked at a veterinary college (small and large animal clinical service departments), specialty practice, private practices, and government sector and is currently an adjunct instructor for the veterinary technology program at Pensacola State College in Pensacola, Florida.

Katy Nelson

USA

1) A veterinary hospital is an inherently stressful work environment. Patients are stressed about coming in, clients are stressed that their pets are ill and concerned about costs. The best trait that any hospital employee can have is empathy. People will misbehave. They will take out their fear or their frustration on you at times. They may yell, they may argue, they may act as if they know more than you do, they may even change their story when the doctor comes into the room, but if you practice working empathetically, you will be more able to tolerate the sometimes inappropriate behavior of the two-leggers who pay the bills. In one hospital where I worked, I had a client come in on emergency with her vomiting dog. The dog was old, had a laundry list of issues, and after the exam and diagnostics were completed, we diagnosed the pup with an abdominal tumor. The client's response to this was a complete surprise to me. She was angry, extremely angry, with me for

telling her this. She began to raise her voice, question my diagnosis, even my degree, at which point I told her I was going to step out of the room to allow her to calm down. I left the room, shaken, and went back into the treatment area where the dog was and began to tell one of my nurses what had just happened. She explained to me that the lady was one of her neighbors and her husband had left her about two weeks before, then her mother had passed away suddenly about five days later. This woman was at the lowest point in her entire life. And I had just told her that her friend of 12 years, her dog, was going to die, too, in the near future. And it was the final straw. I went back into the exam room with an entirely new plan for how to deal with the client and found her crumpled in a corner crying her eyes out. I knelt down, gave her a hug, and we ended up figuring out the best course of care for her beloved pup. And over time, she became one of my favorite clients. You may not always know why people act the way they do, but if you treat them with empathy, knowing that you may know nothing of what's happening in their lives outside that exam room, you will be surprised at how much more tolerant you can be of clients' sometimes erratic behavior.

2) When most people begin their careers, they have a picture in their mind of what their life will be, what their career path will be, and some sort of plan of how to make that happen. But my best piece of advice is to not give up opportunities that come your way because you're so focused on "the plan" you have in place. Allow your dreams to have a little wiggle room. Perhaps you started by working in the kennels, but you think you'd be better at the front desk. Perhaps you started at the front desk, but have your sights set on becoming the one in the white coat. Take every opportunity that comes your way to increase your skill set, expand your knowledge base, and build your resume.

I started out in a regular small animal practice, but transitioned to corporate medicine after a few years. Then, after working for a massive corporation, I went into an emergency practice for almost eight years. During that time, I began to write a few articles, take a few media interviews, and really enjoyed the opportunity to educate people on better care of pets outside of my hospital setting. The media opps kept coming in, and I kept doing more and more, until I actually received an offer to host my own petcentric television show here in Washington, D.C. Now, two and a half years later, my show is still going strong and my career is ever changing. I still practice at a wonderful animal hospital in Alexandria, Virginia, and it keeps me sane and up to date on what's happening in veterinary medicine. I could never have predicted 13 years ago when I graduated that this is the path that my career would take. But because I was open to each opportunity that came my way, and I kept learning, finding ways to increase my skill set, I was ready for each new career option when it came to me. Just because you start out doing one thing, don't assume you'll retire doing that same thing… keep learning, keep your options open, and you may just be pleasantly surprised with how things evolve.

Dr. Katy Nelson was born and raised in Louisiana, where she was blessed to grow up on a farm surrounded by many beloved animals. A graduate of the Louisiana State University School of Veterinary Medicine in 2001, she began her career in small animal practice in North Carolina. From 2003 to 2005, Dr. Katy worked for the Iams Company full-time, and continued her relationship with them as their media spokesperson for many years to follow. In 2005, after getting married, Dr. Katy transitioned back to practice in the Washington, D.C. area.

Her media consulting business began in 2008 after the birth of her first child, and has grown exponentially over the years since, allowing her to work with some of the largest corporations in the pet healthcare world. In April of 2012, Dr. Katy started her own television show on Washington, D.C.'s News Channel 8 called "The Pet Show with Dr. Katy." She covers animal health-related stories on the ABC News affiliate there, as well. She's known as WTOP Radio's "Dr. Pawz," and she works closely with Pet360, PetMD,

SheKnows.com, The Virginia-Maryland Dog Magazine, and numerous others. She practices at BelleHaven Animal Medical Centre in Alexandria, Virginia, is the Chief Medical Officer for Pet Health for Stop Aging Now, and Chief Veterinarian officer for AllergiPal. She lives in the Washington, D.C. area with her husband, their two children, two dogs, and an aquatic turtle.

Tracey Nowers

My mentor once told me, "When you stop learning in your current position, it is time to move on."
I worked in clinical practice as head technician/manager for 20 years. I started working in the kennel, helped with bathing/grooming and eventually worked my way up. After spending many years dealing with vaccinations and neutering, I was feeling unchallenged, but unsure if I could afford to make a change.

Instead of jumping in to a new career path blindly, I started by contacting a specialty practice to see if I could come in and observe occasionally. They offered me a one day per week paid position that would not interfere with my current job. I am glad I chose to try out this new venture before making a permanent change. If I had not, I don't think I could have returned to my previous position in the same venue. I fell in love with internal medicine. Within two years and after much preparation, I was ready to take a financial pay cut (moving out of management and into specialty medicine).
This career change taught me a lot about myself. I have learned so much about exemplary veterinary medicine. I am fascinated by endocrinology. I have had the opportunity to learn how to use the ventilator and how to assist with endoscopy and ultrasounds.

The internal medicine position that I was hired for did oncology about 40% of the time. I learned that I do not like working in oncology. It is hard for me to remain emotionally unattached to chemo patients that I saw weekly for months, and then would have to euthanize. For me, it was like losing my own pet over and over again.

I have since made the change into ophthalmology. This part of veterinary medicine has a language all its own and I am continuing to learn. During this time, I also gained the confidence and experience to become a public speaker. I have spoken at national and state conferences on management, endocrinology, and now ophthalmology. I also have done some consulting on inventory management at local practices.

Although I gave up $7,500 per year in pay, I knew I had to challenge myself to stay happy, and only wish I had done it sooner. I am now working toward my second VTS (veterinary technician specialty). I cannot imagine where I would be if I had not taken that step four years ago.

Tracey Nowers, CVT, VTS, began her love of this career working in a kennel outside of Washington, D.C. She was head veterinary nurse and inventory manager in a clinical practice at the Gardner Animal Care Center, in Gardner, Massachusetts, for 20 years. She especially enjoyed animal nutrition and dentistry. Tracey is currently employed at Veterinary Emergency and Specialty Hospital in Deerfield, Massachusetts, as an ophthalmology technician and is passionate about endocrinology.

Tracey is a long-time member of the National Association of Veterinary Technicians in America and the Massachusetts Veterinary Technician Association, where she was on the executive committee. She also lectures nationally and locally. She is past chair of the Academy of Veterinary Technicians in Clinical Practice and head of the examination committee. She is currently working toward a specialty in Internal Medicine.

Tracey has made several trips with Project Samana to volunteer at spay and neuter clinics in the Dominican Republic. In addition to her work, she has two boys, whom she home schooled. Her hobbies include skiing and snowboarding, snowshoeing, kayaking at the Cape, reading, and traveling with her husband and sons. She currently is owned by three cats: Who, What, and Why, which she fostered as babies.

Louise O'Dwyer USA (UK)

1. Life is like crazy paving

Many people feel that they need to have their lives, including their career paths, planned out like a ladder. In my experience, things never quite work out that way. I have always felt my career path in particular has been more like crazy paving. I never planned on a career as a veterinary nurse, I had an interest in being a veterinary surgeon from a very early age, having always loved animals, but I knew my A-level results would not make this a possibility. I had never really considered veterinary nursing as an alternative. After completing a degree in environmental science and biology, I still had no idea what I wanted to do as my career.

It was a chance encounter with the owner of the practice where I took my own animals that moved my career, and life, in this direction. He asked if I had any interest in "giving it a try." After some thought, I decided that it couldn't do any harm. That was where my career began. After three years in my first practice, working within a team who felt much like a family, and being very happy with my job, I decided I needed something more, I wanted to pursue a further qualification in veterinary nursing. The nurses at the practice told me I would never get any further by moving elsewhere, and that a diploma in advanced nursing wouldn't get me anywhere.

I decided to take my chances. It was the best and most life changing decision I have ever made. I loved working at PetMedics (the practice where I

still work today), but it was honestly the most terrifying six months of my life. I had left a very quiet practice where the nurses carried out classic "nurse" roles: lots of cleaning, reception work, and sadly very little real "nursing" of patients. After six months of learning fast on the job and going home to learn more from textbooks, things became easier. I developed my passion for emergency and critical care nursing and wound management.
I first passed my Diploma in Advanced Veterinary Nursing (Surgical), followed three years later by my Diploma in Advanced Veterinary Nursing (Medical), making me one of the few nurses in the UK to hold both these qualifications.

The practice grew in size and caseload over the next few years and, out of the blue, I was given the amazing opportunity to write my first textbook: Wound Management in Small Animals: A Practical Guide for Veterinary Nurses and Technicians. This opportunity was what started my career in lecturing in continual education to nurses and one that continues to grow still, giving me wonderful opportunities to lecture overseas, as well as in the UK.

Over the past few years, my role had begun to change, taking on more of a managerial role, while still performing the hands-on nursing work that I love. It was the uncertainty of not knowing what was to come that pushed me into undertaking a business qualification - I started a part-time Master's in Business Administration (MBA). That was a HUGE shock to the system. I had never studied any type of business or economics in my life, and it was very, very different from the science-based exams I had completed in the past. Despite the challenges, and undertaking my Veterinary Technician Specialist (Emergency and Critical Care) at the same time, I completed my MBA in 2011. Completion of my MBA meant I could prove to the organization that I worked for that I had the background knowledge in business as well as in nursing. This allowed me to successfully apply for my current position as Clinical Director for the hospital.

My uncertain career path, and the wonderful opportunities I have been given, showed me how important it is to keep an open mind, particularly when working within veterinary medicine. I still hear nurses today saying that it's a dead-end job and it will never get you anywhere. With that attitude, they are certainly right - but with the right attitude, it can literally take you anywhere. As Maya Angelou said, "If you don't like something, change it. If you can't change it, change your attitude."

2. Make time for others
In my experience, people are far too quick to be critical of other people's lack of skills or knowledge, which I find very sad. I'm sure many of us have had a mentor at some point in our lives, someone who encouraged us and inspired us to take a particular career path. The opposite can also apply to people who receive only criticism.

I like to remind people that our knowledge and understanding doesn't appear in our heads by magic, we have to study a subject or be taught about technical aspects of our career by our peers perhaps. If people receive constant criticism, and no support, they will not thrive within their roles. I appreciate sometimes it can get frustrating, but there is a huge reward in knowing you have made a difference to someone, who, in turn, will make a difference to the patients they care for.

The education of your peers is also a wonderful way to educate yourself. For me, writing and presenting lectures is a far better way of learning the information and keeping it inside my brain for any length of time. There is nothing more terrifying than having to stand in front of people and discuss/explain a subject. The one thing you need to do to prepare yourself for this is to know that subject inside out! People will always remember your kindness, in the same way they will also remember your lack of it - and remember that you never actually know where you will be in another 10 or 20 years. People have great memories, and it can only take one incident to taint your career forever!

3. Follow your dreams
In life, it is far too easy to be pushed down a career path, or into a particular job, because that's what

other people want or expect you to do. You have to be determined to get where you want. Life won't always be easy. Women often find themselves juggling between family and career, often with little time for themselves in between. But, if we're honest, if it was easy, it wouldn't be half as rewarding. I think part of the joy in achieving the goals you want to is experiencing difficulties along the way. People often assume I am being modest when I say I am not particularly intelligent, but the truth is I'm not. I have had to work very hard to achieve everything I have. If you don't feel you have the brainpower to get you to where you want to be, think again. Hard work and determination can help you get to where you want to be. Admittedly, it will be tougher than it is for people with photographic memories, but personally I feel you will appreciate it all the more. Struggling with certain aspects of your understanding also places you in an excellent position for educating others. Analogies are an excellent way for me to grasp a basic understanding of a complex subject by breaking it down into more understandable chunks.

Ultimately, I would have to say don't give up on something you really want to do. If you try to live your life to please others, you will never be truly happy, and your lives and careers are going to be long and meandering, so make sure you enjoy the ride!!

Louise O'Dwyer, MBA, BSc (Hons), VTS (ECC), DipAVN (Medical & Surgical), RVN, was born in Manchester UK in 1974. She has had a love of animals throughout her life. Louise went to university in Manchester, gaining a BSc(Hons) in Environmental Science and Biology in 1996. Louise began her career as a veterinary nurse in 1997, qualifying as a registered veterinary nurse in 1997, joining PetMedics Veterinary Hospital, the largest emergency clinic in the UK, in 2000. She progressed to head nurse and now is the Clinical Director. Louise gained her Diploma in Advanced Veterinary Nursing (Surgical) in 2004, followed by her Diploma in Advanced Veterinary Nursing (Medical) in 2007 and Veterinary Technician Specialist (Emergency and Critical Care) and Masters in Business Administration (MBA) in 2011.

Louise has contributed to more than 20 journal articles and books, and lectures regularly on all aspects of anesthesia, emergency and critical care, and infection control. Louise is the co-author of Practical Emergency and Critical Care Veterinary Nursing, as well as Wound Management in Small Animals: A Practical Guide for Veterinary Nurses and Technicians, and the BSAVA Pocketbook for Nurses. Her newest book, A Veterinary Nurse's Guide to Infection Prevention and Control, is due out in 2015. Louise is currently working toward the VTS (Anesthesia) and will sit her final exam in Indianapolis in September 2014, as well as studying part-time toward a PhD in Antimicrobial Resistance in Companion Animals.

Louise holds a position on the European Veterinary Emergency and Critical Care Society's membership development committee, and will take over the position as vice-chair in June 2014 at the EVECCS Congress in Prague. She is also on the British Small Animal Veterinary Association Congress committee. Louise was recently nominated for the prestigious Royal College of Veterinary Surgeons Golden Jubilee Award in Veterinary Nursing, following nomination by her peers.

Vicky Ograin

In vet tech school, we were encouraged to join our SCNAVTA chapter. This is the student chapter of the National Association of Veterinary Technicians in America. It was a great experience being in our student chapter; we helped with events, educated pet owners, and raised money for animal charities. I also developed friendships with my classmates. Being part of this group not only cemented my love for my profession, but gave me a desire to get involved with technician organizations.

When I graduated, I went to a private practice where I was the only credentialed technician. I was so proud to be a technician. I joined NAVTA and was so excited to be able to keep up with what was happening in the technician world by reading the NAVTA Journal. The clinic I worked at was not very supportive of technicians and I often wondered why they even hired a credentialed technician. They tried to have me cut corners with the excuse that "everyone was doing it."

Having the NAVTA Journal allowed me to know that there were technicians in practice doing things the right way, so I maintained the appropriate standards. I was able to get out of the clinic and went into an industry where they were excited that I was a technician. It renewed my faith that being a technician was a worthwhile decision and I was contributing to the well-being of animals. With a renewed sense of worth, I made the decision to get involved. I started by joining the RVT committee of the California Veterinary Medical Association. My job took me to a new state, where I joined the local technician association and when an opportunity to run for a seat on the executive board came up, I jumped at the chance. I am now the secretary/ treasurer of the Kansas Veterinary Technician Association. We are a small organization but growing. I write the newsletter hoping it will help technicians in clinics who wonder what is going on in the profession but don't have access to other technicians. I hope my newsletter helps our members feel connected to our profession.

I have been a technician for 30 years and have always felt connected to my profession through my membership in NAVTA. I never thought I would be worthy enough to be involved on the executive board. I decided to run for the executive board and was honored to win a seat as the secretary. I then decided to go for my ultimate dream; I ran for president and again was honored to win. This year (2014) I am the NAVTA president. To be president of an organization I have so highly regarded all these years is such an honor. I know I will be in this profession for many years to come, but I can't image a higher honor than being the NAVTA president; to be able to give back and hopefully make things better for all technicians and tech students coming in to the profession is an opportunity I will always cherish.

I recommend getting involved with a local or state tech association, as well as the national technician association in your country. You will cherish the experience; it will help you stay connected to others in our profession; it will give you networking opportunities; and, who knows - you may be the next president of your organization!

Vicky Ograin, MBA, RVT, VTS (Nutrition) was born in 1962. She graduated from the Vet Tech Program: Los Angeles Pierce College, Woodland Hills, CA, in 1983. She served in private practice for 18 years in California, and then 12 years ago began a new career with Hill's Pet Nutrition. In 2007, she completed a Bachelor of Science and in 2008, she completed a Masters, both in Business Administration.

Vicky obtained her Veterinary Technician Specialty (VTS) in nutrition in June 2013, and serves as secretary for the Academy of Veterinary Nutrition Technicians. She is also the Secretary/Treasurer for the Kansas Veterinary Technician Association. She is a life member of the National Association of Veterinary Technicians in America (NAVTA), and is the 2014 president. She is also a member of the California Veterinary Medical Association, serving on the RVT committee. In 2011, she received the California Registered Veterinary Technician of the Year award. Vicky speaks nationally and internationally and is a published author.

Julie Paradis

1. If I could do it all over again, I would not have started my career in a specialty practice, but instead would have started in a general practice. I started veterinary technology school with no experience working at a veterinary clinic. During school, I was exposed to many facets of veterinary medicine. I graduated with honors 15 months after starting. I began my career working at a large specialty hospital in the oncology practice. I was so incredibly lucky to get that job and I knew it. It was attractive because it was state-of-the-art and the salary was great for a "green" technician. I worked in oncology for seven years and then worked in surgery for two years. While the experience I gained working at a specialty practice was incredible, it was, well, specialized. I became very good at a limited amount of things.

Nine years into my career, we moved to an area that didn't have a specialty hospital. It was daunting to think about a job in a general practice. It was incredible to realize that what I had learned in school had settled to the deepest recesses of my brain (covered in cobwebs from disuse). I almost changed careers because I was embarrassed that I had been a veterinary technician for nine years, but couldn't remember how to set up and read a fecal and a urinalysis, what the standard vaccines were, and what the life cycle of the flea was, for example. Common medical problems, such as diabetes and Cushing's Disease, were foreign to me. There were medications that I learned about in my pharmacology class that I had never been exposed to and, while the names were familiar, I couldn't remember what they were used for, what the contra-indications were, and what the side effects were. In nine years, new medications had been introduced that veterinarians had been using for years, but I had never heard of them. I was going to have to swallow my pride and find someone willing to re-train me on the basics. I took the plunge and found a wonderful clinic where they were willing to help me shake the cobwebs out of my head.

Now that I have been in a general practice for four

years, I feel that I am a better technician than I have ever been. I have more basic knowledge, which will benefit me when I can return to specialty medicine. I think about my years in oncology and surgery and wish that I had had this basic knowledge then, rather than moving in reverse.

2. If I could start over, I would have asked more questions. When I finished veterinary technology school, I went straight to work at a specialty hospital. The other technicians there were absolutely incredible - they could do so many things, things that I had never even heard of before.
The equipment was state-of-the-art, much of which I had heard about, but never seen or touched.
I had never worked at a veterinary hospital, so all of the exposure I had was from school. I was very intimidated and scared. I had the book knowledge, but not the physical skills and experience to tie it all together.

I didn't want all of those technicians and doctors to think less of me, so while I did watch and learn, I was not very good at asking questions. I repeated what I saw them do, but for a long time I didn't know exactly why I was doing it. This was so foolish on my part, because they all knew that I was a new graduate and would have expected (and welcomed) my questions. Also, I had these elite brains that I could have picked and I could have learned so much. I regret that I didn't take advantage of it, but instead let it pass by me.

After about a year of working there, I was then expected to know the answers to the questions that I never asked, to help train the technicians who were fresh out of school. I could show them how to do everything, but if someone asked me "why," I couldn't always answer and had to defer to others who did know. I realized what I had done to myself and that was when I started to ask the questions. It was so much more painful and embarrassing to ask at this point than it would have been to ask in the beginning.

Now that I do have the skills and experience to tie together with my book knowledge, I feel that I am better equipped as a technician. Now, when I am exposed to something new or have forgotten something, I ask the veterinarian or another technician, without shame. I have seen other technicians doing what I did and I tend to pull them aside and tell them about my experience.

I encourage them to ask as many questions as they can and take advantage of others' knowledge. Books are great, but an explanation as you are experiencing something is invaluable.

Julie Paradis, BS, AAS, CVT, was born in Hannibal, Missouri, in 1972. She has always had a place in her heart for animals. As a child, her parents reveled in asking what she wanted to be when she grew up. Her response until about age 10 was "a dog." Since then, Julie has learned to appreciate cats, too.

During her college years, Julie toyed with the idea of going to veterinary school, but decided to follow in her mother's footsteps and study human behavioral sciences. She graduated with a Bachelor's Degree in Psychology and a minor in Criminal Justice. After numerous jobs both in and out of the field of human behavioral sciences, Julie's passion took over and she returned to the idea of a veterinary career.

At age 27, inspired by T.V.'s Emergency Vets, she relocated to Denver, Colorado, to pursue a career as a veterinary technician and she has not looked back. Julie graduated from Bel-Rea Institute in 2000, first working at the Veterinary Referral Center of Colorado in the Oncology Department for seven years, then the Surgery Department for two years. In 2009, Julie relocated to Little Rock, Arkansas, and began working at Treasure Hill Pet Hospital. After two years, Julie became Office Manager, but she still continues to perform technician duties. When asked if she will pursue veterinary school, Julie replies that the nursing aspect of veterinary medicine is what she loves and she wouldn't have it any other way.

Julie is married and has four wonderful kitty kids who keep her very entertained. She enjoys travel, SCUBA diving, cooking, reading, and hiking.

Helene Pijls   The Netherlands (France)

1. Dare to make a decision and do not be scared to fail. As long as you get up after you fall, you've already won the first battle. Thirty-two years ago, I decided to leave my homeland (France), family, and friends to start a new life in the Netherlands. Such a radical change gave me a lot of opportunities and I tried to take advantage of all these new opportunities.

My first goal was to learn the language. When you know the language, you get the chance to get to know the country inside out, as well as the people and their mentality. Thanks to my drive and ambition, I was able to learn the language pretty quickly, which had the positive consequence that I got my first job in Amsterdam after nine months.

The first part of my work-career had nothing to do with veterinary medicine. I worked for a company that was assisting French companies that were trying to establish themselves or their products on the Dutch market. I was lucky that I understood both France and The Netherlands really well (language, mentality, habits, etc.), which really gave me an advantage. I worked six years for this company. Thanks to my hard workand not being afraid to ask questions, I was able to learn from my mistakes and communicate. Open your mind, arms, and heart to new things.

2. Life is about the people you meet and the things you can create with them. Life experiences made me who I am, just as the coincidences that I faced played a part. A couple times, it was useful for me to forget rationality and just only follow my instinct and my gut feeling. This gut feeling (gut, intuition, instinct - it doesn't matter how you call it) influenced an important part of forming my personality and the way I am nowadays. Just like everybody else, I have made the wrong decisions that were based on rationality instead of trusting my intuition (e.g., making the wrong decision when choosing between two jobs, when supporting people in their decisions, etc.). However, it also happened the other way around.

3. Live your dream, and share your passion. In addition to my roles as a mother of three boys and a spouse for my husband, am I working as the practice manager in a clinic for companion animals. I deal with the employees (veterinarian and the MCA), but also with the customers and their pets. This combination - management and my love for animals - turned my job into my passion.

Do not let anybody tell you that you cannot do something!

Marie-Helene Pijls-Tandia was born in Montargis, France, in 1959. She worked as a medical secretary in Paris (1980) and a stewardess (1981) before moving to The Netherlands in 1982.

In Holland, she worked in various positions: Board secretary at the French Chamber of commerce (1983-1985) and Charge de mission at the French Chamber of Commerce in Amsterdam (1986-1988). She worked with the European publisher "Presses Interuniversitaires Europeenes (1988-1989), as a management assistant at the Euro Business Center in Maastricht (1989-1990), as a commercial/management assistant at "Van Leendert" in Maastricht (1990-1991), and at "ABP" (Algemeen Burgerlijk Pensioenfonds) in Heerlen (1991-1993). She became educated as a CAD technician in Maastricht at the CAD Technician Institute in the South of the Netherlands, and had her own business (1995-1998).

From 2000 until present, Helene is the Practice Manager at a small animal veterinarian clinic in the southwestern part of The Netherlands.

Mikhaele Polaschek   USA

If only I had listened to my instructor from the very beginning, Dr. Bill Fellner, Doctor of Veterinary Medicine in the Animal Health Technology Program at Hartnell College. But I was only 16. I was immensely frustrated with high school and thankfully, with my parents' blessing, I was able to take the test allowing me to graduate early so that I could pursue my dream of working with animals.
Or so I thought.
Dr. Bill warned our entire class of nervous students one early spring day that becoming a Registered Veterinary Technician, or RVT, was not necessarily a lucrative career. I remember thinking to myself

when he said that, "Yes, but I know this is what I want to do…" and "Yes, but I will make good money because I will be the best…" and there were more reasons, too. He couldn't have been more right.

I'm not saying don't follow your dream. I don't regret getting my degree and license.
I am saying it might not be a bad idea to have a back-up plan. Years after graduation, I found out many of my schoolmates had started an entirely different career path not long after they had graduated. Had life not gotten in the way, and had I not married my now ex-husband, I would probably have gone to UC Davis to become a veterinarian and not be stuck today, unemployed, with a mortgage and two young children to care for. Don't get me wrong. Many veterinary clinics can use RVTs. But there continues to be a struggle in veterinary medicine to define the difference between "assistant" versus "technician." A technician should be someone like myself, who exerted blood, sweat, and tears to get through an accredited program and sit for a board exam through the state of California. That title protection should be given and reserved for actual Registered Veterinary Technicians, and preference should be given to those educated as such.

Many clinics would just as soon find a layperson

so they can train them in their own way. You could say there exists a prejudice against schooled veterinary technicians, exponentially reducing my chances of finding work. I am currently toying with other occupations, including police dispatching and postal work. My words of warning are simply an echo of Dr. Bill: becoming an RVT is not necessarily a lucrative career path. Don't go into it thinking every day is filled with puppies and kittens while you roll in millions of dollars. This leads me to my next topic: working with humans.

You would think that entering into the animal medicine field would naturally lead you to working with animals. In a sense, this is true. What I was not taught in school, at least in my mind I was not taught thoroughly enough, was the ability to work with people. I was not forewarned that working with people was an inherent factor in working with animals. Maybe I should have realized this, but I was too young and enamored with the notion and idea of becoming an "animal expert." Yes, in the veterinary field you work with animals, but how many times is an animal attached to a human? A lot!

Animals don't speak to us in the conventional way we are taught to communicate with other humans, so we rely on other humans - namely, the humans who own said animals - to be the voice of the animals in terms of learning what the potential issue may be. This is very important. Please understand that if people cannot communicate, it can lead to unnecessary suffering and heartache. This is true not just in working with animals, but for everyone everywhere. Communication is a key component to our future. I would invite you to ask yourself, "How do I communicate?" At the root of this is a very simple question: Do you communicate through fear, or do you communicate through love? We already know that animals pick up on the fear of humans, but humans also perceive fear from other humans.

Consider this example: a veterinary receptionist is asked to relay charges for services to a client, but the receptionist doesn't agree with some of the charges. In relaying information to the client, the receptionist may exhibit a hesitation, a different

tone of voice, non-verbal body cues indicating her own discomfort. The client perceives this and senses there must be something wrong. The client then starts arguing that the charges are wrong, gets angry, and storms out. Did the receptionist communicate fear or love? In contrast, when someone communicates love, there are no boundaries. There is no fear. Understanding comes much more easily, and the animals also perceive this. There is something else to consider when working with people in the veterinary field, or otherwise. Usually, if someone becomes upset, it is not for the reason you think it is. Be an open, loving recipient of whatever they need to get off their chest. You'll find that, more often than not, their fear-based feelings are not truly directed at you.

Some lasting words of wisdom I wish to pass on to anyone contemplating a career in the veterinary field: you will make mistakes. Do not make the mistake of choosing not to learn from those mistakes. I have made mistakes, I have worked with veterinarians who have made mistakes, other RVTs, assistants, and receptionists who have all made mistakes, and what sets them apart from one another is how they react to mistakes.

Do not make the mistake of locking yourself in a dog kennel with a dog who is eating (I almost lost my finger). You would think that is common sense, but the gate locked inadvertently. Always triple check drug dosages and confirm amounts in the syringe. I had a vet grow irritated when I had asked him to confirm my third dose I'd calculated for a new drug we had in the hospital. When I asked him if he would rather deal with a dead patient, he understood. If a client insists that you don't use a muzzle on their growling dog, let them know that this is how you make a living to support your family, so you would very much like to keep your hand. Better to have hurt feelings than a missing limb. It is okay to question a colleague if you are concerned about something they are administering. You just might save a life. Speak up.

Understanding that mistakes are a necessary component to learning allows for a higher and more rapid success rate. Again, this is not limited only to the veterinary field. When we express greater tolerance for the fact that we are all only human and, know that hard times will come and go, this journey you choose to take will be full and bountiful, and your dreams, whatever they may be, will come to fruition.

Mikhaele Polaschek was born in Portland, Oregon, in 1978. She attended the Animal Health Technology program at Hartnell College in Salinas, California, and graduated Summa Cum Laude with an Associate of Science degree in 1997. After graduation, she pursued her work with small and large animals, pocket pets, avian and laboratory animals, later leading to a teaching position in veterinary technology. She currently lives in Morgan Hill, California, with her two children and a parakeet.

Ingrid Pyka

Interestingly, when I began writing this article, I had trouble assimilating my thoughts. What would I like to have known when I started? What wisdom can I share? A single word popped into my head: Listen. Perfect! This article was going to be easy.

Lesson #1: Listen well and thoroughly before beginning treatment.
I began crafting an ornate article detailing the application of our innate senses - senses beyond the basic sound/sight/feel cues we typically use in the exam rooms. I belabored on increased awareness of word choice, syllabic stresses, and body language. The better our patient and client understanding through inbound input, the higher our level of care. I wrote, re-wrote, read, re-wrote. Still, my words were just not speaking.

Lesson #2: When not using a cloud server, save new documents with the intended file name immediately and resave regularly!
And, additional note to self: When computers freeze up, unsaved documents have a rather nasty habit of vanishing. All of my 1,000+ word draft - gone. I grappled with re-writing the article again, but the low-grade writer's block only grew stronger. Okay, maybe not so easy, I admitted to myself.

So, where was I going with this anyway? Here I am, a veterinarian, turned into a primary business consultant/writer/speaker in non-veterinary industries. What right do I have to spew out advice to people entering the field? Suddenly, my struggles with this essay dissipated. I had a new point, a much stronger message I needed to share.

Lesson #3: Your knowledge and skills can apply to a world of opportunities. Do what you want to be doing.
It seems that most of us begin our veterinary career with an unspoken oath to a life dedicated in its entirety to the animal kingdom. Any deviation from

that path almost seems to cry mutiny against our own meaning. I always had a passion for logistics. What gets results? What doesn't? As veterinarians do, I tackled these questions medically: examine, diagnose, treat, and, on recheck, repeat the cycle. I enjoyed my work, but something was missing.

I soon noticed that my interests increasingly extended beyond animal care. I found myself engaging in stronger administrative roles and taking on more non-veterinary problem-solving. Leaving as associate veterinarian in a small animal practice, I started my own housecall practice, pioneering the full-service mobile alternative in my metropolitan city of, then, already nearly a million. Now hooked on "start-up fever," I immersed myself in emergency clinic turn-keys, working ER shifts as well as much of the behind-the-scenes management and marketing. It seemed like the more exposure I had to business structure, revenues, and strategies, the more rewarding I found my work.

Hold on! When I applied to vet school, this was not the "bunny-hugging" I had envisioned my life to be! What was I doing? I had spent my whole life wanting to be a veterinarian, eight years in college grooming for and finally going through vet school - a coveted slot envied by many like me. Swaying outside pure animal devotion, it felt like I was cheating on my own career. But, I couldn't stop and I finally melded it all together as director of a large, non-profit veterinary hospital. In charge of (and buried in) hiring, training, SOPs, revenue coding, strategy, community liaison - I was loving it. I had chosen this.

My thoughts ruminated about several of my other colleagues: practitioner turned prescription food representative, another a computer programmer, and one more a chemicals researcher. I knew a receptionist who was becoming a human radiology technician and CVTs who were moving into massage therapy. I could go on and on. What did all this have to do with practicing medicine?! Finally, I knew my hang-up! The fact is that seasoned veterinary professionals can and do take on other career paths. And, that is completely okay!

I realized that - probably much like many others in my shoes - I thought I needed permission to stop "being a veterinarian." In reality, I had joined others on a road that molded our astute medical knowledge with our own separate set of skills and passions. It does not mean that we don't love animals or that we can't still serve their cause. Just like one expertly wields a scalpel blade to specialize as a surgeon or another learns the nuances of skin to become a dermatologist, in my case, I was more comfortable with dedicating myself to business structure, to marketing, and to profit/loss statements. In other words, I still use the examine-diagnose-treat-recheck formula I had been so well trained for in animals, instead, for entrepreneurs and businesses! And, I'm still a veterinarian! How awesome is that?!

So, my advice to the veterinarian/technician-to-be or the new graduate: you go do what feels right. The road may be a bit bumpy at times, but you'll sure enjoy the ride much more if you are enjoying yourself.

As my dear high school counselor, Mr. Henry, once told me: "No matter which road you choose, don't ever look back and wish you had chosen the other." My addendum to that is: "No matter where that road does take you, you can always choose a new path to another."

And remember: Listen!

*Raised in California, **Ingrid** moved after high school to Colorado in 1984. She spent her first five years as a small animal veterinarian in Arizona, returning to Colorado to permanently reside near Denver to enjoy the local community, culture, and outdoors.*

Within two years of her graduation from veterinary school at Colorado State University, Ingrid started her own small business in 1994. Doorstep DVM was the first full-service small animal mobile practice covering all of metropolitan Phoenix. She has frequently been featured on radio and television news stories, covering topics from pet safety to new business start-up.

Founder of Beyond Strategy Consulting, a national speaker, writer, and independent publisher, Dr. Ingrid Pyka has held top-level roles in corporate, private, and non-profit sectors. She carries a particular passion for the success of small businesses and their role in today's constantly evolving America.

Focusing on operations management, organization and quality control, she furthered her business acumen through the Veterinary Management Institute at the prominent Krannert School of Management, Purdue University. As Hospital Director at PetAid Colorado, the state's largest non-profit veterinary hospital (formerly Harrison Memorial Animal Hospital), Ingrid combined her greatest passions - helping animals, people in need, and executive management - to reverse ailing systems and a multi-year budget deficit into a positive cash-flow community clinic within 12 months.

Elizabeth Reed

Throughout my career, I have had a plethora of learning experiences, and I expect to have a lot more! Some of those experiences have been good, and some have been bad. The key is to make the best of all situations and to learn from them. I try not to repeat the bad mistakes and hopefully others can learn through my experience!

First, the best career choice that I have made thus far is completing my bachelor's degree in veterinary medicine. Although there are countless opportunities for a technician to pursue in the veterinary field without a bachelor's degree, my career has catapulted further because of finishing that journey. I knew after 8 years of working as a veterinary technician that I wanted to eventually move over to the veterinary industry side. When I started looking for positions, I realized that the minimum requirement to join the industry is a bachelor's degree. Being a single-income technician, I could not afford to quit my job and go back to school full time. Therefore, I researched online programs. St. Petersburg College accepted all of my RVT classes and applied them toward my BS degree. Thus, I began the online education track. Along my journey, I recruited four other RVT class-mates to join me in getting their BS degrees as well. It was fun and encouraging to have some of my same classmates chatting together in my online classes. We also were able to help each other with online projects and even save money by swapping and sharing books.

Second, besides making an excellent decision by getting my BS degree, I can also admit the worse decision I made. As a new RVT graduate, I became a bit arrogant and acted like I knew everything. I definitely offended some on-the-job trained veterinary assistants when I first graduated.

It was okay for me to be proud of my accomplishment because there was so much that I did learn in only two years of school. Yet there is so much more to learn once you are out in the workforce.

There is no possible way to learn everything at school in two years. Veterinarians cannot even learn everything in their four years of school. The hard lessons I learned are these: remain teachable, ask for help, and be willing to learn from anyone. No one knows everything. Medicine is a constantly evolving field, and realizing the value of learning from others is a key to quick success.

This leads me to my third piece of advice, which is to network like crazy! As I mentioned about learning from others, I have often found that, "It is not only what you know, but who you know." Creating professional allies and friendships will allow you to succeed. A part of how I was able to obtain a position with Royal Canin was through my professional networking with a rep from Royal Canin, and he introduced me to his hiring manager.

There are numerous opportunities to network and be involved in the veterinary field. Here are a few examples: attend as many CE opportunities as possible, get involved with a veterinary technician association on the state level and run for an executive board position, get to know industry reps in the area, and utilize them to grow in knowledge of a specific area of interest, and stay in touch with past classmates. The veterinary community is a very small community, and the longer one is in it, the smaller it gets. Do not burn bridges, no matter how unprofessional others may act. Be the bigger person.

Lastly, everyone needs a driving passion. Find your passion! Find what drives you and interests you in the field of veterinary medicine. If you like nutrition, pursue it! If you enjoy monitoring and assisting in surgery, find out how you can do better!

"Everyone can rise above their circumstances and achieve success if they are dedicated to and passionate about what they do." - Nelson Mandela

Elizabeth Reed, BS, RVT, CVT, CCRA, was born in 1983 and is a dedicated Texas native. She has been working in the veterinary field for more than 13 years. She graduated from Cedar Valley College's Veterinary Technology Program in 2004 and the Canine Rehabilitation Institute in 2007. Her experience ranges from small animal to large animal, exotics, emergency and critical care, canine rehabilitation, teaching at three community colleges' veterinary technology programs, end of life care, canine reproduction, and most recently, she has moved over to the industry side of veterinary medicine and is a District Manager for Royal Canin Veterinary Diets. Elizabeth finished her Bachelor of Science in Veterinary Technology in 2012 through St. Petersburg College.

Elizabeth has been published in numerous magazines, journals, and books. She also has been a speaker on the subjects of End-of-Life Care and Canine Rehabilitation at several state and national conferences. Elizabeth won the prestigious RVT of the Year award in Oklahoma in 2009 and is the current Treasurer for the Executive Board of the Colorado Association of Certified Veterinary Technicians.

Rebecca Rose

1. Get your Credentials, "Just DO IT!"

Upon graduating from Colorado Mountain College in 1987, I began working at Town & Country Animal Hospital in Gunnison, Colorado. I recall traveling to Fort Collins, literally five hours of driving over the mountains and through the woods, to take my Board Exam. At that time, it was a five-hour test, to include written, oral, and practical portions. Thankfully, I passed and became a Certified Veterinary Technician in Colorado. I worked as a CVT on the floor in a busy, three-veterinary practice for seven years. We did it all in the rural, mixed-animal setting and my doctors were great teachers and team advocates. Then, I became the mother of my second child and my life changed. I was no longer able to work full-time and support the daycare demands,so I allowed my certification to lapse. Familiar story?

Fast forward to 1997 and I began working at Town & Country full-time again. I wanted to renew my certification. As it happens, it was either pay extended fees and show proof of Continuing Education or retest. I chose to retest!

I spoke with Dr. Schick about my desire to retest and we came up with a mutual agreement that the clinic would pay for the certification test and I would sign on for two years. It was a win/win situation. I was IN! For the next four months, I studied for the exam. Everyone knew of my goal at the clinic and it became a bit of a team effort. I divided my studying into segments, making sure to focus on the testing categories being offered on the new National Exam. Since I felt pharmacology would be the most difficult, it was the largest focus. I can remember pouring hours of study time reading McCurnin's text book. Finally, the weekend of the exam! I drove over to Denver, another four-hour trip over the mountains and through the woods, for my second testing. Now the exam was 200 questions, multiple choice. Needless to say, I PASSED! I not only passed, I did better the second time around!

The point is, if I can sit for the test, 10 years after graduating from college, and pass, so can you! As you may know, to sit for the Veterinary Technician National Exam is more convenient than ever before. If you have graduated from an American Veterinary Medical Association (AVMA)-accredited program and decided not to test, I encourage you to take the exam. If you took the VTNE once and didn't pass, I encourage you to take the exam. If you have allowed your certification, registration, or license to lapse (regardless the reason), I encourage you take the test. Do you see the reoccurring theme here? I ENCOURAGE YOU TAKE THE TEST!

There are support groups on various sites, plus Veterinary Support Personnel Network (VSPN) has an eight-week course to prepare you for the exam. Now, you have no excuse, get your credentials! If you have questions or need help determining what your next move is regarding the VTNE, consider visiting the Association of American Veterinary State Boards (AAVSB) to locate the organization in your state to move forward.

I support you and know there will be others in your sphere of influence who will support you, too. As the Nike ad suggests, "Just DO IT!"

2. Live Courageously

My favorite motivating picture is a photo of a courageous pig hang gliding. Kind of like the cliché "when pigs fly," all things are possible! Often times, veterinary team members ask me about career growth and professional development. My advice: the sky is the limit and you are only limited by your own imagination. Truly, if you can design a career direction, chances are you can create it and bring it to fruition. It will take time, dedication, focus, commitment, and tenacity.

There are so many career options available to you within veterinary hospitals and beyond - so many, in fact, that there is a book titled Career Choices for Veterinary Technicians, Opportunities for Animal Lovers. There you will find that technicians now have 11 choices to become a Veterinary Technician Specialist, opportunity be a Certified Veterinary Practice Manager, and titles for nearly every aspect in veterinary management. Consider becoming your clinic's Social Media Coordinator or Life-Stage Expert. If your job description needs to be updated to include new skills and passion, I encourage you to speak with your supervisor or manager and design a new career focus. Career choices beyond the hospital include industry, education, consulting, self-employment, and even the government.

I dare you to live courageously and follow your passion. Sure, there will be obstacles, but know there are also ways to overcome barriers. Look around you. Within the veterinary community, there are many veterinary technicians who have fulfilling, creative, rewarding jobs. Jobs they have turned into sustaining careers that bring them great joy, financial support, and challenge them to continue to grow. Search out a mentor or career coach, belong to and participate in your local veterinary professional organizations, network and GROW your career!

There are numerous resources to help you along the way:
- Veterinary Support Personnel Network (VSPN): *www.vspn.org*
- National Association of Veterinary Technicians (NAVTA): *www.navta.org*
- Catalyst Veterinary Practice Consultants: *www.catalystvetpc.com*
- VetTechLife: *www.vettechlife.com*

and MANY, MANY MORE! Choose which venue and group is best for you and live courageously, follow your dreams, and reach your greatest potential! Never stop learning and continue to grow in your professional development within the veterinary community.

3. Know state laws that govern the veterinary profession

This may sound really boring and stuffy, although I feel it is important to be informed and engaged in understanding the rules, laws, and regulations that govern veterinary medicine. Laws can be clear as mud, enormously confusing at times. Very few individuals make the time to educate themselves on this crucial aspect of a career.

Rebecca Rose, CVT, was born in 1966. She graduated from Colorado Mountain College in 1987 with an AAS in veterinary technology and became credentialed as a Certified Veterinary Technician in the same year. For the past 25+ years, she has been serving the veterinary community. When looking back upon her diverse career, Rebecca has worked as a veterinary technician at a mixed animal practice, offered relief

services throughout Colorado, was the first paid administrator to the Colorado Association of Certified Veterinary Technicians, managed two AAHA veterinary practices, and works with various industry leaders in an array of areas.

In 2002, the Colorado Veterinary Medical Association (CVMA) honored Rebecca with their Veterinary Technician of the Year Award. In 2011, the CVMA awarded her with Industry Partner of the Year award. During the Association of Veterinary Technician Educator's Symposium in 2013, Dr. Scott Keller recognized Rebecca for her valued contributions on the Local Symposium Committee.
AAHA Press recently updated her book, Career Choices for Veterinary Technicians; Opportunities for Animal Lovers. This one project opened up many doors of opportunities. She encourages other veterinary team members to take their career to new heights by stretching themselves and stepping outside of their comfort zones. She also writes peer-reviewed articles for Veterinary Team Brief, has works appearing in TECHNEWS, and contributes to veterinary technician program textbooks.

Nadine Rust   USA (South Africa)

During my seven-year journey in the veterinary profession, I have had the pleasure of many educating experiences and opportunities for advancement. I have been asked, and am honored, to share my experiences and thoughts with the growing veterinary community. The following bullet points are concepts I have found to be true during my time as a veterinary technician. I have included some personal experiences to further support these concepts.

1. Find what motivates you.

I'll begin with a concept I have found helpful not only in my professional life, but in my personal life as well. Find what motivates you. Whether this means finding a mentor, or following a thought/activity that motivates you to further your knowledge base and skills - I urge you to cultivate it. I believe finding a mentor would be your best option. Self-motivation is admirable, but difficult to maintain. A mentor will not only help you aspire to greater heights, but also help guide you toward your goals more efficiently.

2. Be diverse.

What do I mean by this? Simply put, be capable of performing and have a basic knowledge of all aspects of your job description. Be a "jack of all trades." Focusing on a specialty that you enjoy is encouraged, but always make sure you can be useful in whatever your job entails. This not only makes you a more valuable employee, but also helps ensure job security. At the start of my career, I made sure to gather all the knowledge I could from every source available. I was fortunate enough to have colleagues and superiors willing and able to teach me all the intricate details of my profession -

or tricks of the trade. By showing my willingness to learn, I became a trusted member of the team. Consequently, I was asked to be a part of their Blood Bank team and to be a surgical technician for their orthopedic surgeon. While my focus lies in orthopedics and blood banking, I remain proficient in all aspects of radiology, surgery, dentistry, emergency care, and general nursing care. Be sure to practice your least used skills as often as possible to remain dexterous in all of your learned abilities.

3. You CAN teach an old dog new tricks.

The worst team member is the one who believes they are omnipotent. Being open to new ideas and information will leave room for growth and development in a field that is continually changing, a wonderful and sometimes tedious trait of the veterinary world. Staying on top of continuing education opportunities is a great way of attaining new information and skills, but learn all you can from your colleagues and superiors as well. There are always six different ways to do any one thing, and this is true for just about everything, so knowing multiple ways and finding what works well for you, is the best way to go. One more thing on this matter, it is possible to learn from someone who is new to the field. Not only have I gained insight and information from technicians fresh out of school, I also have had the opportunity to teach technicians with 10 years more experience than myself, demonstrating that knowledge can come from anyone at any level.

4. It's okay to say no.

Too often, technicians, and other veterinary team members, are asked to perform a task they may not be comfortable with. This can range from restraining fractious patients, taking non-sedated radiographs on unruly pets, working with uncooperative clients, performing a duty you believe will be harmful to a patient, etc. Remember, it is acceptable to politely refuse and express that you are not comfortable with performing the task. There were several instances when I should have said no but didn't, and consequently I ended up bitten or scratched - one of those times resulted in a lengthy hospital visit for a very painful rabies vaccination. Avoid lengthy hospital visits. Many times, all that you

need to do is make the appropriate individual aware of the situation, such as requesting sedation for radiographs, so do not be afraid to speak up. No harm can come from expressing a concern.

5. Remember, the community only functions if you work as a team.

I cannot stress this point enough. While some duties can be performed independently, most of your work will require the help of your colleagues. Always be kind and accommodating to all members of the staff and you will find that any task becomes significantly less stressful; peers from all departments become more supportive and willing to lend a hand when you need it. If not, you will find yourself alienated in a world where you cannot afford to be. There will always be individuals who will be unwilling or unable to acclimate, but try not to be one of them. The flow and efficiency of any hospital or clinic is greatly improved when the staff can come together as a functioning team.

6. Separate professional from personal.

Your professional life is an integral part of who you are, but so is your personal life. Becoming engrossed in advancing in your career can be intoxicating and you will find yourself doing little else. Always, always, always make time for your friends, family, and - most importantly - yourself.

Never allow what may be happening in your personal life to affect your work. Keep the two separate. This is a lesson I unfortunately learned the hard way. I was so busy trying to reach my professional goals I did not realize how much I was distancing myself from my friends and my loved ones. Avoid unnecessary stress by finding a good balance between the two. Something I find useful is to take "mini" vacations throughout the year.

Whether you plan a cruise to the Bahamas or just take a long weekend to spend with those you care about, make sure it is time spent free from your work, both mentally and physically. You will find, as I have, that you will be much more successful in both your personal and professional life if you learn this lesson early.

I have the sincerest hope that my words provide a positive, motivating, and helpful insight to any team member of the veterinary community that takes the time to read them. Best wishes to any and all intellectuals/professionals in the veterinary community family. May your future endeavors be successful and prosperous.

Nadine Rust *was born in Pretoria, South Africa in 1988. She began her college career in 2004, seeking an Associate's Degree in Biology at Broward Community College, which she completed in 2006. Soon after, she started her professional career at Hollywood Animal Hospital as a volunteer, which turned into a permanent position as a veterinary technician in 2007. A year into her career, she was offered a position in the Hollywood Animal Hospital Blood Bank, and, again, soon after that, she was offered a position as one of Dr. Jon Dee's personal technicians. Nadine still fills both of these positions. During the development of her professional career, she pursued a Bachelor's Degree in Biology at Florida Atlantic University, which she completed in 2014.*

Elizabeth Salan USA

1. I wish I had realized how physically demanding this job is!

Being a vet tech is physically and emotionally exhausting. Lifting, bending, restraining, standing on your feet for multiple hours at a time, sometimes not getting any sort of break to eat lunch or dinner, working overtime, working overnight, dealing with traumas and emergencies - all of these things take a tremendous toll on the human body. I was a little more aware of how physical this job is since I worked as a veterinary assistant in an emergency hospital before attending school to become a certified veterinary technician. I think everyone who is interested in becoming a vet or a vet tech should spend some time in a veterinary hospital, whether as a veterinary assistant like I did, or in a volunteer capacity. It's not all vaccines on cute puppies and kittens and dentals on cats. It's a lot more than that. It would be ideal to go into this career path in top physical shape as a young person. But with more and more veterinary technicians entering the field after having other first and sometimes even second careers, age and physical fitness are factors that need to be taken into account. We're not all going to become vet techs right out of high school at our peak physical age; therefore, we need to take good care of ourselves. Eat right, have regular sleep routines (especially important for those who end up working overnights), work out, get regular massages, practice yoga, whatever it takes! And most of all - listen to your body! Don't try to be a superman or a superwoman and lift an 80-pound dog by yourself. Wait until you have help, even if it means taking a little longer with that particular appointment. Veterinary technicians are particularly prone to developing lower back issues, including bulging discs and sciatica. Lift smart! Know your limits!

You will have a longer and healthier career if you take care of your body. Good shoes are an important part of your vet tech uniform. A good pair of shoes, such as Danskos, are well worth the investment. Some hospitals will provide a stipend for uniforms, so take advantage of it! Gyms will often provide companies with discounts for gym memberships, which I highly suggest taking advantage of. A healthy, happy, and balanced vet tech will be able to be a vet tech for a lot longer.

2. Volunteer, volunteer, volunteer!

They say that the average lifespan of a technician in a veterinary hospital is 7 to 10 years, but I have known technicians who burn out long before that. I was in the midst of feeling just such a burn out about five years ago as a CVT, so I started looking for different opportunities. One of the things I looked into was international volunteering, which was cost prohibitive for me at that time. But the international veterinary volunteer search led me to domestic veterinary volunteering, which led me to the Humane Society Veterinary Medical Association/Rural Area Veterinary Services (HSVMA/RAVS), and this has changed my life. HSVMA/RAVS travels to Native American reservations throughout the United States and offers free spays, neuters, and vaccinations.

My first volunteer trip was a weeklong spay/neuter/ wellness clinic to the Spirit Lake Reservation in North Dakota. As a veterinary technician, I was responsible for helping with the surgeries (as many as 45 to 50 in one day), participating in the wellness exams, communicating with the owners, among many other things. I also helped the veterinary students with anesthesia, placing catheters, recovery, injections, and so on. In teaching the future vets, I found myself becoming excited about veterinary medicine again. Seeing how grateful the owners were helped remind me why I got into veterinary medicine in the first place - to make a difference. Not only did I meet amazing people from the reservation itself but I also met veterinary professionals and students from all over the country. The vet students make up the bulk of the people on a trip such as this and they can range from students just finishing their first year of vet school to the recently graduated doctors.

Working so closely with future vets helped them understand the value of veterinary technicians and helped ensure a respect and understanding that will, hopefully, last throughout their careers. You don't have to look far to volunteer if traveling is not for you. Volunteer at your local shelter or rescue. Talk to your local elementary school about speaking at a career day or career fair. Get out of your comfort zone and you will quickly remember why you got into veterinary medicine in the first place.

3. Get the highest degree that you can!

I wish that I had finished school and gotten my bachelor's degree. The higher your degree, the higher your pay - as crass as that may sound. If you chose not to pursue a higher degree, then specialize! There are numerous different specializations you can look into - anesthesia, surgery, clinical practice, equine, behavior, nutrition - to name a few. The more you specialize, the more valuable you become as a technician and the more doors will be open to you in the future. Even if you don't pursue further education or specialization, you owe it to yourself and your patients to keep learning. Most hospitals have a continuing education allowance for their technicians and if they don't, it is definitely something you should suggest. Attend as much CE as you can! Veterinary medicine is an ever-changing, ever-growing field and it's very easy to become outdated as new techniques and new medicines are introduced. Stay current and knowledgeable about veterinary medicine. A good, often untapped resource for new information would be recently graduated veterinarians. They often have just learned about new trends in veterinary medicine and are eager to share their knowledge.

Elizabeth Salan was the first author contributing her career learnings to the VetTeamCoach project on 17 September 2013.

Elizabeth Salan was born in Northern Michigan in 1977. She began her career in veterinary medicine as a veterinary assistant at the Animal Emergency Hospital in Grand Rapids, Michigan, before deciding to become a credentialed veterinary technician. She graduated from the Bel-Rea Institute of Animal Technology in Denver, Colorado, in 2004, passed her national board exams to become a Certified Veterinary Technician and started work at Alameda East Veterinary Hospital shortly thereafter. Elizabeth had many roles while working at Alameda East, including lead technician in the Treatment Department, as well as the Intern Coordinator. In 2010, she made the move to become an instructor at the Bel-Rea Institute, where she is currently teaching Comparative Anatomy I and II, Sterile Techniques, Large Animal, and Veterinary Science II.

Oreta Samples USA

went to work, later being hired back by my alma mater as Lead Vet Tech. Wow, what a coup that was. It was not until I had the chance to work with students who were now matriculating through at the same frantic pace that I finally saw truly that it has to be about the knowledge - the grades and proud accolades were second to actually being able to do things right for my patients or, in this later case, for my technician students.

Youth is synonymous with passion. Everything we do when we are young is approached with rapid-fire passion over the subject matter, the person, the career; the list goes on and on. But at the end of the day, when joints creak a bit more and the back stiffens up... well, we begin to learn that life is about the little things and the passion-filled impatience to be first no longer matters. It's doing what feels right that matters most whether it be in our personal or professional life... now that feels good.

When working toward my degree, it was all about grades and dates. Life was a frenetic pace of activity that never slowed down. I graduated and

Oreta Marie Samples is a licensed veterinary technician who currently is employed as a lecturer and Program Coordinator within the Department of Veterinary Science and Public Health at Fort Valley State University, Fort Valley, Georgia. She is a graduate of the same institution, where she not only received her Bachelor's Degree in Veterinary Technology (1994), but also her Master's Degree in Public Health (MPH) (1995). She hails from the USA, where she has been a life-long resident of the state of Georgia. Oreta has spent the majority of her 19 years at FVSU teching, teaching, and writing professionally and hopes to be a "freelance writer" when she grows up. She enjoys professional speaking and networking at veterinary conventions, writing for scientific publications, and, of course, her # 1 passion, reading - both visually and audio. In her spare time, Oreta enjoys painting in the watercolor medium, watching old movies, and sharing time with friends and fur-babies - of which there are currently seven.

Carolyn Shadie

USA

1. Learn the "Soft" Skills. They are the Hardest.

Many years ago, I lived next door to a young veterinarian who had graduated only six months before. I was also a recent grad, serving in a new role for me as instructor in human communication.

My neighbor confessed to me that she'd always loved animals and could "talk" to the dogs and cats with great ease. Talking to the clients, however, was not so easy for her. Most of her academic life had been spent mastering the sciences, which she had to do to get into vet school. The idea of taking a psychology or sociology course seemed quite foreign to her, and she'd never heard of a course in interpersonal communication.

I invited her to attend a series I was teaching. She came, and she was blown away.

First, she tried her newfound skill of "reflective listening" on her four-year-old daughter. "What a difference," she said. The power struggles seemed to melt away.

When she realized that she could take time to listen and then empathetically respond to her husband, she found that he talked more and told her more about what was on his mind.

Then she had the opportunity to listen to a client. He was upset about his dog's health, as well as the unexpected cost of the care. She said that when she responded with "reflective listening," she was able to respond with confidence. She knew then that she'd found a skill that would give her more comfort in talking to her clients.

I lost contact with her after the course was over, when I moved away. When I saw her two years later, this is what she told me: "Learning listening skills changed my career and maybe my marriage, too. What was becoming frustrating began to become pleasurable. I only wish I'd taken some "soft" skills courses before working. Those skills are really "hard"!

It was many years later that I had the opportunity to address this topic in Trends magazine, published by the American Animal Hospital Association. My husband, who is also schooled in communication arts, joined me in creating case studies that enable veterinary staff to grapple with common communication challenges that arise among all veterinary staff members. Ultimately, some of the cases were combined in a training resource entitled Communication Case Studies: Building Interpersonal Skills in the Workplace. If you haven't had time to master the "soft" skills along with the vast amount of medical knowledge you need to do your job, I encourage you to find the time. I think you'll find that it will make your job easier.

2. It's About Listening.

Listening, it turns out, is a skill. Who would think it? But, yes, listening is not so easy as it seems, and there are two parts of the message to listen to.

It starts with silence. Sometimes it takes discipline to remain silent while someone else is talking.

You have a similar story to tell or a piece of advice the other person could use. It's so tempting to jump right in. Instead, try remaining silent.

While you are silent, you have a chance to listen. Let your conversation partner know that you are listening. Eye contact helps. Perhaps leaning in will say with your gesture that you are attending to her words. An acknowledgement of her with a comment like, "Uh-huh," might also reassure her that you are listening.

Listen for both parts of her message: content and feelings.

Often the content is clear, but sometimes you should check to see if you got the facts right. After giving her plenty of time to complete her thought, you might paraphrase her comment to check your understanding with, "Are you saying… ?" or "What you're saying is… ."

Feelings are more difficult to "hear," but when you can identify the feelings behind the content, you are hearing a more complete message. Just as you may communicate with eye contact and gestures, the person talking to you will also often express her feelings through her body language, as well as her words. Pay close attention to both. If the facial expression or gesture doesn't match the content of the message, chances are the non-verbal message is the right one. Either way, you need to check your understanding. When you've "heard" the feelings, it is useful to decode them and respond based on what you think you have heard. You might say, "You sound very anxious about…" or "I sense that you are quite worried. Am I right?"

If your perception is wrong, she will correct you. She will, however, appreciate your attending to her message. Your response will indicate your desire to determine the essence of her message. Instead of advice or a correction or telling your own story, your comment says, "I want to understand. Tell me more. I'm listening."

Carolyn C. Shadle, PhD, currently writes and trains for the veterinary profession. She has written extensively for the American Animal Hospital Association, including as co-author for the popular series of communication case studies in Trends magazine. She also co-authored Communication Case Studies; Building Interpersonal Skills in the Veterinary Practice, published by AAHA.

Through ICS, Inc., she provides training, writing, and consulting to equip adults with the skills and tools to build effective organizations and healthy relationships. She has worked in university-based adult and continuing education at California State University, Long Beach, and San Jose; the University of Denver College of Business; and the State University of New York (Buffalo and Empire State College).

Carolyn earned a Bachelor's Degree in History at The College of Wooster in Ohio, (and a year at the University of Geneva, Switzerland), a Master's Degree in Religious Education at Union Theological Seminary in New York City, and a PhD in organizational and interpersonal communication at the State University of New York at Buffalo. She has written numerous publications, hosted a TV interview show, and offered training in communication, planning, and change for corporate, public, and non-profit audiences, as well as for parents and grandparents. She also raised two daughters, who were the guinea pigs for many of the concepts and skills in communication that she teaches.

Carolyn grew up in Washington, D.C., and has settled in La Jolla, California. Since retirement from university administration, she has devoted herself to her continuing interest: communication training. She and her husband, John Meyer, PhD, who also has degrees in communication arts, maintain websites and blogs at www.ICSinc.info and www.VeterinarianCommunication.com.

Allie Smith

1. Dealing with humans

One thing I have learned over the years working in the veterinary field is how to deal with the pet owners who come into the practice. Many people get into this field because they love animals and love working with and helping animals. What many people forget is that with those animals come pet owners. Nobody should ever say that they don't like working with people and that's why they want to work in the veterinary field, because without the pet owners, we would not have our jobs.

What I have learned about dealing with pet owners is to put myself in their shoes and think how I would feel in this situation. It is very nerve racking to have your pet taken from your side and "into the back" to have treatments or diagnostics performed. The owner recognizes the nervousness from the pet, usually a result of being in an unfamiliar place with so many different smells, and that nervous-ness from the pet transfers to the pet owner.

When I am about to take a pet away from the owner, whether it be for a blood draw or to admit the pet to the hospital for surgery or hospitalization,

I always assure the owner that we will take excellent care of the pet. I'll mention that Mary is in the back and she just loves Chihuahuas and will be so excited to meet "Fluffy." If the pet needs to stay for a period of time with us, I will tell the owner that "Fluffy" will have a big, thick comforter to sleep on while in her cage and that she will be staying in the area of the hospital where someone will always be on duty, so she will have close supervision and be treated extremely well.

If your hospital has the ability, taking pictures of the hospitalized pet while the owners are not there is a great way of making the client feel at ease that: "Fluffy" is safe in our hands. We will sometimes send a text message to the client with a quick update and picture. Adding pictures of the technicians cuddling with the pet on discharge instruction sheets is another way to ease the pet owner's mind.

2. The notebook

A few years into my career as a veterinary technician, I became an "In-Patient Technician" responsible for all of the hospitalized and ICU patients during my shift. This was overwhelming at first because I could be in charge of one patient or sometimes as many as seven. It was my responsibility to make sure their treatments were completed on time and they were cared for appropriately. I was also responsible for applying the appropriate charges for each patient during my shift, writing discharge instructions, and updating clients on the patient's status when they called. Sometimes, the doctors would be requesting multiple treatments or diagnostics for multiple patients and I needed to keep this all straight so the patient was being cared for properly.

I came up with an idea to have a small pocket notebook on me at all times during my shift. At the time of shift change, we would do rounds on all of the hospitalized patients with the technicians and doctors. I would use this time at the start of my shift to jot down notes about each pet. Each page was dedicated to one patient. I would write the signalment of the patient at the top of the page. I would make notes on the current problems that we knew the patient was having. I would jot down things I wanted to monitor during my shift, such as appetite or respiratory rate. I would make notes about any charges I needed to apply to the patient's invoice and then cross them off after I had entered them. This little notebook provided me with a method to double check that I completed everything properly and also ensured that I was not compromising patient care.

Allie Smith graduated from Centenary College in Hackettstown, New Jersey in 2007 with a Bachelor's Degree in Equine Science. After graduating college, she started working at Princeton Animal Hospital, a canine/feline general practice in Princeton, New Jersey. Allie passed the VTNE in 2009. Currently, at Princeton Animal Hospital, Allie works as a Hospital Coordinator and works with both the in-patient and surgical teams. She is responsible for new employee training and training of interns from both Mercer County Community College and Manor College. She has also written articles for Veterinary Technician magazine. Allie is working on her VTS in Clinical Practice for the 2014 case year.

Carin Smith

These suggestions are for anyone on the veterinary team.

Make yourself valuable to the practice. This is a business that must be successful to continue to treat animals. While the practice owners do care about you, their primary concern is that the practice remains successful. Help them do that by asking what you can do more, differently, or better. Look for opportunities to take on new skills or knowledge in medicine, communication, management, and leadership. When you make the practice more successful, the practice will value you more.

Maintain boundaries. Be clear about what is acceptable to you. If something isn't right, set aside a time to talk directly with whoever is involved. Do this even though it is difficult! However, prepare ahead of time so it's not just a gripe session. Be specific about what is happening and what specifically you want to be different. Then offer to help make that change happen. If that isn't possible, look for a job in a practice that is a better match.

Stay on good terms with everyone. If you are in a supervisory position, be friendly but avoid close friendships since that could be viewed as favoritism by the others. Maintaining this approach from the beginning, when you first accept a job, is easier than trying to undo a situation that has gotten out of hand. If you are not yet a leader, you may someday be one. Anticipate that and manage friendships carefully.

Pitch in and help. Make a point of noticing when something needs to be done, and do it. Spend more time with pitching in than you do with thinking about what others are or aren't doing to help.

Many veterinary team members work part-time. If that is you, then put extra effort into clear communication between shifts. Arrange for overlapping shifts so you can let others know what is going on that day. Show up for team meetings.

When you are at work, focus on work; when you're at home, focus on home. That way, each of your priorities gets the attention it deserves!

Dr. Carin Smith, *President of Smith Veterinary Consulting, works to help veterinarians and their teams create successful lives and careers. She is a facilitator, speaker, trainer, and author who gained experience in both large and small animal practice before devoting her time to her current work. In 2010, she received the Distinguished Service Award from the Association for Women Veterinarians, and, in 2014, she was asked to serve as a writer for management questions on the North American Veterinary Licensing Exam. Dr. Smith is a nationally recognized, award-winning author of hundreds of articles and many books, including Team Satisfaction Pays: Organizational Development for Practice Success, and Client Satisfaction Pays: Quality Service for Practice Success. She is co-author with Rebecca Rose, CVT, of Career Choices for Veterinary Technicians: Opportunities for Animal Lovers.*

After participating in the VetCoach project in 2013, Dr. Smith launched the idea to start the VetTeamCoach project to share career learnings with "all team members working in the veterinary practices, clinics, and hospitals." She convinced Rebecca Rose and Richard Nap to do it. This book is the result.

Brandy Sprunger USA

1) That the bullies don't matter.
Those who wish to bring you down do not matter;

they will not affect your career in the long run. They know they are bullies, other employees and their bosses know they are bullies. What you are experiencing nearly everyone else in this profession has experienced - but that does not in any way make it okay. You will spend many a day worrying about whether you are in the right profession, since clearly these bullies don't think you should be, so maybe they are right? Know that the bullying is really their response to the perceived threat that you are to them - whether you are trying to be a threat or not, you are. This is actually a good thing because it means you are outstanding in your skills and knowledge and they know they can't keep up. Keep your head held high and keep learning. Don't let others bring you down, and if they do, don't be afraid to approach them. They've been waiting to be approached, so be the first one to do it and pave the way for future employees in your same position. If the supervision in the clinic does not manage these people appropriately, you need to find a new clinic, plain and simple. On the flip side, don't be the bully; don't be a skills hog or an information hoarder. This does nothing for the practice, for your coworkers, or for your patients except make you look like a bully. Share your skills and knowledge willingly and freely.

2) To keep learning.

Don't let your only education be your Veterinary Technician associate's degree. Go for the bachelor's degree, learn how to educate people, find a topic you are passionate about and learn more about it. If there was something unusual at work you've never seen before, look it up! Do it on your own time so there are no distractions. Work doesn't (or shouldn't) always stop just because you left the building. Don't let the only continuing education you obtain be from drug representatives or journal articles. Get out there and spend some money on a good conference (and sometimes it is your own money, but you are investing in yourself!).

Be inspired to learn more from those conference speakers - in fact, be inspired enough to BECOME a conference speaker. Don't get just enough CE credits to maintain your license; make the Examining Board sift through all those extra hours! Get your VTS in something you love. Use online resources as well to get CE, such as VSPN.org or Facebook, but also learn from your colleagues. We don't all do things the same way, and this is a GOOD thing. Make sure you surround yourself with supportive people, and then set some goals and achieve them (this will also help handle #1)!

3) How to network.

It's not just for software engineers and politicians, it is important for veterinary technicians as well. You made it to a big conference, but don't go back to your hotel room until you've made some new friends. Step outside your comfort zone and go to a reception where you don't know anyone, meet people from other states in other parts of the field. Keep those connections. Friend them on Facebook and then meet up with them again at the next conference. Follow some online groups and post on message boards - put your name out there so that others recognize you. Vent a little to those who are in your shoes. Give advice to those who

are new to the field. Networking is how you build your career and find new avenues to pursue. Should you ever choose to leave your current practice, you have colleagues in other areas waiting for you to join them in theirs (this helps handle #1 and make #2 more fun)! And have a good hand-shake - you will get more compliments than you know how to handle.

4) That you CAN make money as a Veterinary Technician.

We all heard when we were in school that we would always live paycheck to paycheck; that we'd never make much more than minimum wage. Don't stand for this because they were all wrong. If you are aware of the prior three things I've listed and achieve them all, you will make money in this career. You might have to move to a new specialty hospital, you might have to leave your current city or state for somewhere with more opportunity, you might write an article, you might teach on the side, you might lecture at those conferences you've been going to. These things are where the money is. Don't let general practice be the only thing you do for your entire career if it's not where your heart is. Don't settle for a job that is not challenging. If you use your network, the extra money comes even faster!

I learned these four things on my own, or I heard them from people like my father, but I never believed or truly listened to them. When I first got into veterinary medicine, I thought general practice was where I'd retire. I had no idea at that time I'd be standing up in front of an audience of my peers at national and international conferences sharing the knowledge I've collected over the years.
I learned these four things because I dared to go to a conference on my own, because I dared to sit in receptions and conference parties and make a point to introduce myself - difficult for someone as introverted as myself. But it is what has led me to meet such amazing and inspiring veterinary technicians, and to be as successful as I am today. I love my colleagues, and the ability I have to share my knowledge and skills with them. And THIS is what makes you a professional.

Brandy Sprunger has worked in the veterinary field since 1995. She has worked for zoos and general practices, and has been in emergency/critical care since 2002. She recently made the move to teaching while continuing to work in clinical practice as a relief technician. She has authored articles for several websites and journals. She is also a Board Moderator, Course Assistant, and Book Reviewer for VSPN.org, and has reviewed textbooks for the NAVTA Journal, as well. Brandy was a founding member of the Veterinary Health Care Team of Arizona and is a member of the Veterinary Emergency and Critical Care Society (VECCS) and the National Association of Veterinary Technicians in America (NAVTA). She has also been the State Representative to NAVTA for both Arizona and California, and, in 2005, was the Arizona Veterinary Technician of the Year. Despite being a credentialed veterinary technician for more than 10 years, she recently graduated from Mesa Community College with her AAS degree in Veterinary Technology, and passed the VTS exam in Emergency and Critical Care in 2012. She provides hands-on labs and lectures for her coworkers and students, and began lecturing nationally in 2012. Her passion is providing interesting, relevant, and challenging continuing education to her colleagues while also working to elevate the status of the veterinary technology profession and the capabilities of veterinary technicians around the world.

Jenny Sullivan USA

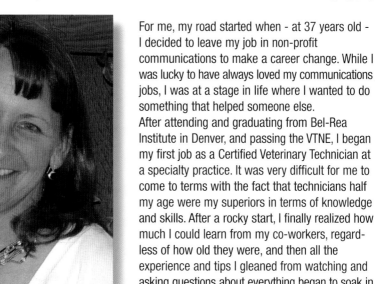

For me, my road started when - at 37 years old - I decided to leave my job in non-profit communications to make a career change. While I was lucky to have always loved my communications jobs, I was at a stage in life where I wanted to do something that helped someone else.

After attending and graduating from Bel-Rea Institute in Denver, and passing the VTNE, I began my first job as a Certified Veterinary Technician at a specialty practice. It was very difficult for me to come to terms with the fact that technicians half my age were my superiors in terms of knowledge and skills. After a rocky start, I finally realized how much I could learn from my co-workers, regardless of how old they were, and then all the experience and tips I gleaned from watching and asking questions about everything began to soak in.

The Road Less Traveled

Robert Frost, the epic American poet, wrote: *"Two roads diverged in a wood, and I / I took the one less traveled by, / And that has made all the difference."* My road in veterinary medicine has been that road less traveled by, but I wouldn't change a thing. Instead, I would urge you to look at all the roads open to you as you begin this journey.

While it's unusual to encounter older technicians who are career-changers fresh out of school, I would urge you - if this is your situation - to not lose heart. Yes, you may be used to being an experienced professional in your previous career, but now is the time to practice some humility and learn everything you can from everyone you can, regardless of their age or position. Skills you've already mastered in a previous work environment will serve you well if you're willing to start over.

A takeaway I had from my previous career in communications was a freelance business as a writer and editor. In many ways, this made it possible for me to take an enormous pay cut to become a technician, because I knew I had another source of income that paid well. As time went by, I was able to parlay that freelance business and gain some new clients in the veterinary field. I've written numerous articles for veterinary and animal-oriented publications, helped write and edit marketing materials for clinics and hospitals, and even worked on larger veterinary or animal-related projects - including editing this publication.

A freelance side business is an excellent way for technicians to combine the things they love and augment their incomes. Figure out what skills you have that could be useful in other aspects of a practice and use them to your benefit.

Because I started working as a technician at an older age, it became clear to me right away that the physical toughness of the technician job was something that would be harder for me than for my 20-year-old colleagues. This led me to look at other options for staying involved in this field that I loved without sacrificing my body. The large specialty hospital I worked in was also home to a branch of one of the major veterinary reference labs in the country. After several years, I applied for and was offered a position as a lab technician. I loved that I still felt a part of the diagnostic aspect of veterinary medicine. I felt like I was helping to put together the pieces of the puzzle for each case we tested.

Remember that there are many rewarding roads in veterinary medicine, and being a clinical technician isn't the only road open to you.

I found bountiful rewards down the less traveled path - and wouldn't have had it any other way.

Jenny Sullivan, BA, AAS, CVT, was born in Hanover, New Hampshire, in 1961. Growing up with sheltered, rural New England roots that ran very deep, Jenny graduated with a bachelor of arts degree in English from Dartmouth College in 1983 and was ready to head for adventure. That meant moving across the country to Denver, where she worked in academic publishing, corporate communications, and non-profit publications for 15 years.

In 1998, Jenny decided to have her mid-life crisis early and get it over with. She left her job and attended Bel-Rea Institute, where she graduated in December 1999 with high honors, receiving an associate's degree. In January 2000, she got her first job in the field, working for the Internal Medicine Department of a large specialty animal hospital. She also took and passed the VTNE.

Through the years, Jenny worked in several different areas of veterinary medicine: from small animal general practices to an equine hospital to various specialty medicine areas, and finally landing in a branch office of a large, California-based veterinary reference laboratory. Jenny had an opportunity to combine her love of writing and publishing with her love of animals by moving into the Managing Editor position of an equine magazine in 2008. She currently works outside of the field as a Technical Editor for an engineering firm, but continues to pursue freelance projects in the veterinary field, complete CE requirements, and maintain her CVT credential, even though she's not working in the field currently.

Kristy Sweetland USA

As a 20-year-old Registered Veterinary Technician, I was eager and excited to begin my career in veterinary medicine after having completed a two-year program in veterinary technology. I remember those early days. I was wide eyed and a little unsure of myself. The veteran technicians seemed so confident and capable; it was very clear I was to stay out of their way. I followed their lead with every detail. Even the new DVMs who began with us seemed a little afraid of these no-nonsense nurses who seemed to own the hospital.

I was one of those who entered the field because I loved the animals. Pure and simple. Every euthanasia made me cry, every smashed up hit-by-car made me sick with empathy. At first, I felt no need to hide my emotions. When I felt like crying, I cried. Just a silent tear or two, nothing distracting. My expression was unique enough back then that the veterinarians I worked with began to request me for every euthanasia. They liked it that I cried in the exam rooms; it was comforting to the clients to know that we truly cared.

As my career progressed and my confidence increased, I began searching for greater challenges.

I took a job in a busy emergency hospital in urban Minneapolis, and then I relocated to New England, where I worked for board-certified surgeons and internists. As the challenges became greater, and the years went on, I learned to get a little "harder". In the high-volume specialty hospitals, I learned to keep up, not cry. There was no time for emotions and if the senior technicians saw me wiping a tear, they'd label me as "soft." Bad things happened to soft technicians in teaching hospitals.

By now, as a 30-year-old woman, I was managing the surgery department in a referral hospital, training young technicians who still cried. One incredibly busy day, one dog with a broken femur sat in a kennel waiting for his pain meds and another item on my to-do list read "euthanize Buddy." The veterinarians were as busy as I was, everybody running to keep up, but there sat those two dogs… just items on a technician's to-do list. I froze when this realization hit me. How much pain must the Labrador be feeling, with a femur broken in two places? What about the ancient cock-a-poo waiting for his euthanasia, his family too distraught to stay and wait with him? What must he be feeling? When this realization hit me, it was like somebody punched me in the stomach. I stopped and for just a very stressed minute, had a good cry for these two dogs for whom I had been too busy to advocate.

Something clicked in me then. I realized I had lost my perspective, slowly, over the years. I gave in to the pressures of a school of thought which believes that to be efficient, to be sharp, you need to be callous. This school of thought believes there's no time to "feel" and that there's nothing worse than a "soft" technician. I took back my identity that day, and became a more authentic expression of myself. I worked another 10 years in the field and never again did I allow a euthanasia to become just another item on my to-do list. Never again was I too proud to cry.

There is a place for our hearts, our feelings, our empathy in even the most challenging of environments. No matter how busy we get, each little patient in front of us, each family entrusting us with their loved-one, deserves our entire presence, not just our analytical capacity. I wish someone would have reminded me of this from the very beginning. If I had to do it all over again, I would have declared my heart my guiding North Star, every day.

Kristy Sweetland *grew up in the beautiful state of Colorado, where her love for animals quickly evolved to a life's passion. She knew from the very beginning she was born to work with dogs and cats in some capacity. Throughout her childhood, her focus never wavered. Graduating with an Associate's Degree in veterinary technology, and then going back to the University of Minnesota to earn her Bachelor's Degree in psychology, Kristy spent 20 glorious years in the field of veterinary medicine as a Registered Veterinary Technician, working in general practice, emergency, and referral medicine before she took a corporate position in veterinary toxicology. For the last 12 years of her career in vet medicine, she worked in administrative/management roles that included the mentoring and coaching of her employees. She came to love this facet of her work more than anything.*

Today, Kristy holds a Master's Degree in Transpersonal Psychology from the Institute of Transpersonal Psychology, currently known as Sofia University, in Palo Alto, California. She is a published author and a Certified Professional Coach, ICF ACC credentialed. With the focus of leading individuals to recognize their own passion and purpose, her work is intuitive and skilled, bridging hidden aspects of self back into communication with the light of our awareness. Here, transformation takes place, which creates the foundation for authenticity, productivity, freedom, and creativity. Through Kristy's process of deep listening, powerful questioning, gentle guidance, clarity, and laser focus, a person's truest self learns to shine and lead, unhindered, unafraid, and exceptional in all areas of life.

From her office in beautiful Santa Fe, New Mexico, Kristy works with private coaching clients locally and all over the world in-person, by phone, or via Skype. She is happily married with three beloved cats and two cherished dogs. You can find her at www.CoachingToComeAlive.com.

Angela Taibo USA

After working in the veterinary field for close to 30 years, I have learned a variety of life lessons that have guided me to become more successful in what I do. I began volunteering at an animal hospital when I was 11 years old. My parents were asked to sign a waiver stating they understood the risks of my working in a clinical setting, and that's where my experiences began. The very first lessons I learned were those of professionalism and hard work. I would watch veterinarians, veterinary technicians, and volunteers come and go because of their lack of humility and professionalism. The vets and techs who were willing to work in areas outside of their job descriptions excelled and stayed employed at the clinic. Technicians who were willing to answer phones, handle reception work when needed, and clean cages or walk dogs were an asset and were considered open minded and hard working. We knew they were here for the love of the animals and the success of the hospital. Veterinarians would be willing to answer phones when things got busy. I watched the metamorphosis of a growing hospital and happy staff. I knew that if I were to succeed, then I would need to learn to multitask.

The second valuable lesson was to never sit still. When I was volunteering, I would be given a list of tasks to complete each day around the clinic. If I completed my tasks before quitting time, then I would never stand around waiting for someone to tell me what to do. I would find things to do on my own. I would take initiative. This is a lesson my mother instilled in me that has guided me well in practice. I would anticipate what needed to be done and then go and do it. I didn't wait to be asked. I didn't brag that I completed more tasks than those on my list. As I progressed from a volunteer to an assistant and then to a technician, I maintained this personal rule. It helped to create a pleasant working environment.

My third lesson deals with professionalism. In this technological age, it can be very easy to put your foot in your mouth. We can easily be braver posting something online instead of saying it in person. I've observed these instances over the past few years. Disgruntled students or employees will post rants on Facebook and Twitter. Many times, they believe that only their closest friends will see these posts. However, the veterinary community is a very small world. People forget to consider how others might perceive what they write. I've seen countless graduates and former employees struggle to find work due to this lack of common sense. While others may share in your frustrations and opinions, you must try to separate your personal and professional lives. Online communities make it more and more difficult to find that fine line. This is why I refuse to have Facebook and Twitter accounts.

My fourth lesson is that there is no such thing as the perfect job. When I began volunteering, there were times when I became frustrated with the job or with the people and considered quitting. Coworkers would annoy me or I would disagree with the way something was handled at the clinic. I would see others with the same frustrations quit without even having a second job in place. My mother would tell me, "There's no such thing as the perfect job," using her job as an example. And she was right! You have to take the good with the bad. Eventually, the people who annoyed me that I disagreed with would leave, either fired or quit, and then new coworkers would start and things would get much better. There were always highs and lows.

After working in practice for 16 years, I decided that it was time for a change. Just as in practice, I still see people struggling with the same issues. I'm content with my professional life and can't imagine it any other way. As people come and go at work, I sit back and look at all I've achieved thanks to those early life lessons.

Angela Taibo, BS, AAS, CVT, was born in Houston, Texas, in 1974. She is a first generation Cuban-American. After moving to Colorado at the age of 11, she began volunteering at Wingate Animal Hospital. During her 16 years at Wingate, Angela progressed from being a volunteer, to a veterinary assistant, and finally to a veterinary technician. During this time, Angela saw a lot of changes, including Wingate becoming the second Colorado hospital to be sold to Veterinary Centers of America (VCA). Shortly after graduating from both Bel-Rea Institute of Animal Technology (1998) and the University of Colorado at Denver, BS in Math and Biology, with emphasis on secondary education (2000), Angela decided to try a different challenge by going into human medicine as a phlebotomist and medical laboratory assistant. After receiving a call from a former instructor at Bel-Rea about an opening as an instructor, Angela's teaching career began.

Ms. Taibo has been teaching at Bel-Rea for 13 years in subjects including Hematology, Parasitology, Clinical Chemistry, Anatomy Lab, and Medical Terminology. In March of 2014, Angela will have her first textbook published: Veterinary Medical Terminology Guide and Workbook.

Nanette Walker Smith　　　USA

1. I always knew I wanted to go into medicine; the healing arts always intrigued me for as long as I can remember. Because I had doctors, nurses, and dentistry in my family, but I loved animals, I spent time as a teenager volunteering for every aspect in our community hospital to get a wide exposure to human medicine. I realized I loved almost every aspect of medicine, but also realized animals were my preferred focus. I researched veterinary schools, what type of individuals they were looking for, included Latin and German in my foreign language repertoire (which has continued to be beneficial as an educator and a mother), and remained active in my community. I determined I wanted to attend the same school for my bachelor's and doctorate degrees. In retrospect, the desire not to move during school overshadowed possibilities of me attending a less competitive school early on, might have improved my concentration and GPA, and I may have succeeded in getting accepted to veterinary school. However, my chosen major, zoology, fit me

perfectly. I not only graduated in four years with a Bachelor of Science degree in Zoology, but with a minor in German. Throughout college, I chose activities close to my intended veterinary career by volunteering at the veterinary school giving tours and was hired on as a kennel aide for the small animal ward. This gave me good exposure to a hospital setting, but did not give me much in the way of all-around learning. When I was not accepted to veterinary school on the first try, I turned to a couple of my professors/mentors, one zoology and one veterinary anatomy, for advice. I would be a zoologist now if my mentor had not already turned in his retirement paperwork. The "how it all works together" completely fascinates me still and is central to how I teach my students and my children, seeing things from a larger perspective as a collaborative of shades of gray rather than black and white. The veterinary anatomy professor hired me to work in his lab, my first foray into the computer digital era, and prompted me to look into AVMA-accredited animal health technology. Unknowingly, I didn't realize there was such a field, even after working at the veterinary school hospital! The time spent researching my intended field of interest, determining my major of study based on what really interested me, utilizing mentors, and putting myself into situations that would maximize my ability to learn helped prepare me for veterinary school, but also helped prepare me for what happened when I didn't get in to veterinary school.

2. Diving into understanding animal health technology/veterinary technology I went backward and received my Associate of Science degree, got deeply involved in credentialing, the importance of skilled and educated learning, and never looked back. I was fortunate early in my career to get a job at a very prestigious 24-hour emergency, specialty, and general practice near the AHT program

I was enrolled in, but only after I literally begged to use them as my summer externship and witness multiple aspects of veterinary medicine. Dr. Denny Nolet and Deb Turpin, RVT (one of the first technician practice co-owners) were my mentors and placated my desire to maximize my summer learning. I worked my rear off! But I showed them I was dedicated, reliable, a go-getter, and not afraid to ask if I didn't understand. When I returned to school that fall, I had launched myself so much farther past my fellow classmates, my instructors had me demonstrating techniques to the class (…enter the teacher). I married into the active-duty military late in life and added two children to the mix after that. This allowed me to have a very firm hold on my professional life: years on the local, state, and national veterinary technician committees and connections throughout the veterinary world via the specialty practice led to Paul Pion, co-founder of the Veterinary Information Network™. After starting as a volunteer on VIN's Veterinary Support Personnel Network in 1993, I became a part-time, then full-time employee, eventually overseeing all of VSPN as the Content Director. During part of that time, I spent 13 years building and growing VSPN continual education (CE), which provides a means of continuing professionalism to support staff worldwide - you can never learn enough.

3. Opportunities are funny, often coming out of left field, and can be scary. If anyone had told me I would work as a vet tech primarily on computers I would laugh. However, the world skills I've learned by observing and paying attention to more than just my job have allowed me to grow in knowledge and be a reliable resource for answers or for direction where to get the answers. I have also seen the veterinary technology field continue to grow and expand exponentially, making it feasible for the veterinary technician to find a niche in which to perfect his/her dream job: making a difference in animal's lives magnified by adding another (or several) of ones' interest(s) or abilities. I'm sure I would be happy as a veterinary technician had I not taken a few calculated leaps of faith to find my niche. Leaps of faith can be the log at the edge of the cliff with the great unknown on the other side. Or the leap of faith can include a GPS, Google Map, and print out of area information and identification to help calculate the leap - at least a little bit, especially when the landing involves a family, well-being (physical and mental), a career (past, present, and future), and ultimately the next step to personal success! To borrow from an old quote, "There is no 'i' in TEAM." I can honestly say that, throughout my life, there have always been a number of people, both professionally and personally, who have been there to listen, guide, teach, and support me. Nothing is ever achieved as a singular person "I," for it is always a TEAM effort that creates the true success. There are times the title of DVM would be advantageous to get attention, but I find it is not always the degree, but the professionalism, experience, and how information is presented that makes the difference; the degree can be a bonus OR a hindrance. The days of "doctor, lawyer, Indian Chief" as job choices are long gone. I have my niche: I get to be a veterinary technician, an educator, a dreamer, a resource, a counselor, and a mentor almost every day - and I love what I do!

My next foray is now knocking at the door, and I'm working on re-calculating my GPS and potentially adjusting my niche just a bit.

Nanette Walker Smith was born in Boulder, Colorado, in 1964 and grew up in the Colorado Rockies. She, husband Dave, and two daughters live in Colorado with a rescued Great Pyrenees, two rescue cats, and assorted fish. She holds a Bachelor's Degree in Zoology from the University of California, Davis; Associate of Science degrees in Animal Health Technology and Environmental Design-Architecture from Cosumnes River College; and a Master of Education-Vocational Education (emphasis on Adult Education and Community College Administration) from the University of Central Florida.

Nanette's veterinary experience includes the UC Davis Veterinary Medical Teaching Hospital (as an under-graduate); Sacramento Veterinary Surgical Services in Sacramento, California; Pinedale Animal Clinic, a mixed-

animal practice in Wyoming, and teaching at the AVMA-accredited Brevard Community College Veterinary Technology Program (now Eastern Florida State College). As a volunteer member of the Veterinary Support Personnel Network (www.vspn.org), Nanette was asked by Paul Pion at Veterinary Information Network (www.vin.com) to help revitalize VSPN in 1993, then, with the VSPN Team, help re-launch VSPN in 1996. In 2000, as a VIN employee, she and her fledgling team launched online CE for support staff through VIN, which has since grown to more than 50 courses per year incorporating all levels of veterinary medicine and practice management. Nanette was employed by VIN for more than 15 years, growing VSPN membership from 30 to more than 40,000 members, facilitating resources, content, discussions, and much more for the veterinary support community.

Along with helping those in the profession realize and achieve their dreams, Nanette has been extremely active in veterinary technician and veterinary medical association functions. She served 12 years in the Sacramento Valley Veterinary Technician Association Board and the California Veterinary Medical Association-RVT Committee; served a term as Vice President of the North American Veterinary Technician Association (NAVTA); co-founded and served on the Board of the Wyoming Veterinary Technician Association; served on the Florida Veterinary Technician Association (FVTA) Board; and maintains active membership in national associations: NAVTA and AVTE (Technician Educators), and state veterinary professional associations: CACVT (Colorado), WyVTA, CVMA (California), and AVTA (Alaska). Nanette has been continuously involved in the veterinary field for more than 25 years, maintaining credentials in California (RVT since 1988), Wyoming (CVT since 2000), Colorado (CVT since 2009), and Alaska (LVT since 2005).

Laura Ward USA

What I learned from more than 20 years leading and managing veterinary health care team members:

I've managed and led two highly successful and innovative veterinary clinics for more than 20 years. One of the most valuable lessons I learned early in my career was how to recognize each team member's individual strengths and weaknesses and how to integrate them into a team. The first step I take when I'm evaluating a new hire is to have casual conversations that probe into their pet care beliefs and experiences; attitudes about work, responsibility, and advancement; and traits they look for in managers and coworkers. I ask these questions in a relaxed, non-threatening manner and in a genuine bilateral conversation. In other words, I have a list of questions I want to ask in mind and I have a conversation that allows the new hire to share his or her needs without the formality of an evaluation or closed-door discussion. I believe many managers have these conversations and acquire much of the same information; they just do it in a more random, time-consuming, and less efficient fashion. The answers to these questions are vital for me to learn how to motivate the new employee and which team members to pair them with for training.

I believe the value of an employee is much more than simply measuring their productivity, skills, and length of employment. A successful team member also must lead others, be creative, and overcome daily adversity and challenges with a positive attitude. My husband and business partner, Dr. Ernie Ward, refers to our best employees as "headache-free". By this, he means the most valuable employees do their job well and don't create "headaches" or unnecessary problems with other team members, doctors, or clients. I agree; no manager likes headaches. Reward the employees who consistently arrive on time, do their jobs well, and make those around them better. That makes my job of bringing out the best in the team easier and allows me to improve our service and productivity.

I strive to help my team members recognize their individual behavioral style, as well as the behavioral traits of their coworkers. Self-awareness is key to self-control and learning to contribute confidently to a team. We work in an environment where emergencies, emotional outbursts, and unexpected events are normal. If you have team members who regularly lose control of their emotions, you undermine morale and efficiency. Understanding my team's personality traits helps me control the workplace mood and assign the best person to each situation.

Finally, I only ask my employees to do what I do. I have found that leading by example is one of the essential traits of good leaders. If you expect your receptionists to treat each client compassionately and warmly, you must treat both your clients and staff with compassion and warmth. If you value a professional appearance in your staff members, you must dress the part yourself. If you advocate for good nutrition, you must feed your pets the foods you believe are best. If regular blood and urine tests are what you recommend to your clients, your personal pets should be tested once a year. Veterinary clinics are a direct reflection of their leaders. I demand excellence first from myself, then from my staff.

I hope these quick tips will help guide you toward better leadership and a more harmonious, cohesive team. Learning to be a better manager is an infinite challenge. After more than 20 years in the veterinary profession, I'm just as excited, energized, and challenged as I was on the day we opened our first clinic. I wish everyone in our great profession the same great career and lifelong rewards.

Laura Ward was born in 1967. She attended the University of Georgia, earning a Bachelor's Degree in Education and a Master's Degree in 1992 in the field of Speech-Language Pathology. Prior to her career in veterinary medicine, she worked in human healthcare in various clinical settings. Laura is a veterinary practice consultant for E3 Management, a veterinary education company. Laura and her husband, Dr. Ernie Ward, are previous owners of Seaside Animal Care, a nationally recognized small animal clinic and DogGone Healthy, a facility dedicated to improving the social, emotional, and dietary needs of pets. Under her leadership, Seaside Animal Care received a Hospital of the Year Award and was an AAHA-accredited facility dedicated to excellence.

DeeAnn Wilfong

Asking what you wish you had known during a specific time in history is a hard question to answer. If I had known then what I know now, would I have made the same choices that led me to where I am? Would I be someone else, somewhere else? As I thought about what my answer should be, I revisited nearly 15 years in the veterinary industry and decided on some noteworthy items that would not necessarily have changed the course of my history but sure would have made a lot of it easier. I only hope that it can help you in your journey.

Network, network, network. Do not mistake this for having an impressive number of social media friends. Social sites are great tools for keeping in touch with the people you already know, but networking requires face time, and not the kind Apple provides. As I write this, I realize that every position I have had in veterinary medicine I earned because I stood out among other qualified candidates because of who put in a good word for me. This person was not a reference, but instead was the person the hiring clinic called because they knew that person knew me, and they trusted that person's opinion. Every position.

Start by staying in touch with your classmates, instructors, and mentors. You never know when you may need their expertise, their honest opinion, or their good word (as mentioned above).

Attend conferences and talk to everyone you meet. Make it a point to talk to the most random people at conferences, you never know who you might meet. Don't be afraid to use something or someone in common to make a connection. Use that business card you're dying to give away, that's what they are for. The veterinary industry is very small and interwoven; don't underestimate the power of that infrastructure. Instead, tap into it, become a part of it, utilize it.

Get to know your co-workers and stay in touch with them as you pursue career advancement. They will do so much for you. They will challenge you to be better. They will give you a sense of belonging. They will be your support when something doesn't go right. They will drive you crazy. One day, you may walk into a practice and find a former co-worker is your new boss.

Spend time with the students you encounter. They will someday (soon) be your peers and it's great when they share fond memories of you with others. They will challenge you to know your stuff because if you don't, they'll be onto you in a heartbeat. While that is often intimidating and even annoying, it will challenge you to be better. Keep your mind open to their thoughts and ideas. They will see things differently and may be able to offer a solution you hadn't considered, or you might be able to further their education by telling them why it won't work.

Remember names. To hear someone say, "I'm just not good with names," only tells me they are lazy. Remember studying for exams? If you passed, it's because you took the time to study, enlisting tools and endless tricks for recalling that information. As veterinary professionals, you not only need to know your peers' names but your clients and their animals as well. I promise you, if you can refer to a peer by name (without an obvious glance at their nametag), greet a client by name and refer to their animal correctly you have just made a large deposit in the emotional bank. To remember peoples' names requires study, tools, tricks, and some work. Respect your peers, clients, and patients by calling them by name.

When things go wrong, ask yourself, will this matter in five years? I discovered this nugget of wisdom through a co-worker who I actually couldn't stand to work with. At the time, I constantly worried about the details that weren't being managed and the work that needed to be done. My co-worker was much more laid-back, had fun at work and was a generally positive person. I resented her attitude because I felt she didn't care about personal work ethic or responsibility to our patients. One evening, I heard her relay this question to a co-worker who was upset over a disagreement with another co-worker. I thought about it and realized that there is very little in our day-to-day lives that will change the course of our future in five years. I'm more than five years past my time with her and she was right, most of what I worried about then doesn't matter now.

Work/life balance. Strive for it, negotiate for it, insist on it, have it. I'm going to tell you something you don't want to hear as a new graduate... this (veterinary medicine) is just a job. Before you decide that I have no idea what I'm talking about and discount my words, hear me out. Veterinary medicine is hard. Lives can hang in the balance, clients are emotionally charged, and that's before anyone brings up money or practice management. It is also something you have chosen to do; you are not required to do this for a living. It's okay to be a veterinary medical professional and work at Starbucks, no one is stopping you. Life is the entirety of what is happening to us, which means our chosen profession only gets to be a percentage, a piece of the pie. It's a sad day when you realize the one thing defining you is your role in veterinary medicine. I encountered that sad day when I was making significant career choices in an effort to balance life. I was hit with the realization that I didn't know who I would be if I wasn't a part of this industry, if I let my specialty status expire, if I no longer attended national conferences. I had become solely defined by what I did for a living. That's not balance.

Finally, take pictures of all your cases. Fun ones, cute ones, scary ones, hard ones. You'll thank yourself (or me) for having them when it comes time to present the cases.

DeeAnn Wilfong, BS, CVT, VTS-EVN, was born in 1974 and grew up in a small town in the southwest corner of Wyoming. She attended Idaho State University in Pocatello, Idaho, originally as a pre-vet student. During her studies, she decided to forego a veterinary school application and, instead, focused her biology studies on wildlife. During that time, DeeAnn worked at Ross Park Zoo (now Pocatello Zoo) and intended to follow a zoo/wildlife biology career path. While in her senior year, she decided that she still had a strong interest in veterinary medicine. She switched gears and was accepted to Bel-Rea Institute of Veterinary Technology in Denver, Colorado. She graduated in 2000 and immediately went into an intensive equine internship with Littleton Large Animal Clinic in Littleton, Colorado. DeeAnn survived and was offered a staff position in their Intensive Care Unit. She was the lead technician in that unit for five years before deciding to take a position in the Internal Medicine Department at Rood & Riddle Equine Hospital in Lexington, Kentucky, where she spent her time focused on neonatal medicine, neurology, and infection disease cases.

After deciding to move back West, she accepted a position in the Anesthesia Department at Oregon State University in Corvallis, Oregon. There, her focus was still equine/large animal but expanded to include small animal anesthesia for cardiology, internal medicine, and orthopedic cases. She was eventually offered the chance to return back to the Rocky Mountains and accepted a position as the Head Technician at Littleton Equine Medical Center (formerly Littleton Large Animal Clinic). For the next five years, DeeAnn led a staff of 23 technicians and assistants, while working in the Anesthesia and Imaging Departments.

During her years in equine medicine, DeeAnn was a member of the executive board of technicians that created the technician equine group AAEVT, and the executive board that created the equine technician specialty group AEVNT. Additionally, she was one of the first equine technician specialists in equine nursing (VTS-EVN).

DeeAnn has been a guest speaker at several national and local veterinary conferences. She has been published in technician journals and has co-authored and co-edited AAEVT's Equine Manual for Veterinary Technicians. In 2013, DeeAnn made some life changes and left equine medicine. After taking a few months off, she accepted the Hospital Manager Position with Cheyenne Mountain Zoo in Colorado Springs, Colorado, and is currently enjoying the challenges of working with zoo animals.

Jennifer Wiseman USA

1. Managing grief

No matter how many times you read or hear about how to handle a client in grief, you will never fully understand what it entails until it happens to you. When I attended school, I was never allowed to assist with a euthanasia. I believe they thought that it took someone with a little more experience and an adequate amount of maturity to handle that kind of situation. While I totally agree with that assessment, it took me a lot of time in the field to learn how to handle the client's emotions as well as my

own. Now, after many years of experience, I know to expect the unexpected but always be attentive to clients in their time of need.

Each client reacts differently to the loss of a pet. Some clients will cry, while others remain silent, and then there are those who tend to be grateful that it is over. There will be clients who want to tell you all the cute anecdotes about "Spot" or how they used to bring home chicken nuggets from McDonald's for "Fluffy." They'll tell you how their pets saved their life, and how they were a terror as a puppy or kitten but became a great friend in the end.

No experience is ever the same, but the vast majority of these clients are unprepared for the loss of their pet. While I've rarely seen the anger stage of grief at the clinics where I've worked, I nearly always find an overwhelming sense of sadness. These clients need me to share in their sorrow, and I do my best to help ease their pain. I make eye contact and respond to their questions and comments. I laugh at how "Spot" chewed up the remote or nod at the story of how "Fluffy" woke them at 3:00 a.m. when there was a fire in their house. I want them to know that their pet was special not only to them, but to me (even if I've never met "Spot" or if "Fluffy" tried to take my fingers off). I do have difficulty keeping the tears at bay at times, but it is worth it to see that sense of relief when they realize that I understand what they are going through.

The rewards I have are few when it comes to euthanasia. There is no rainbow at the end, and unfortunately, there are days when you have more than one to deal with. However, I have had my fair share of hugs and the occasional pat on the shoulder as the client leaves the room. It may not be much, but it is enough to know that I made this hardest decision a little easier. I can honestly say that I am glad I was able to offer the slightest comfort when those clients needed it most.

2. Supportive care for the parvo puppy

When a parvo puppy comes through the door of our clinic, we can't help but worry about contagion. Our brains automatically turn to the well-being of any animals that might walk in the door that day. While this reaction is totally understandable, we should also consider the client and the puppy's feelings regarding this virus. Our job as veterinary professionals is to educate the client about parvovirus, but I also believe that our first priority is to put ourselves in the patient's paw prints.

Consider this: Milo is a six-week-old Rottweiler puppy with five siblings. He leaves his home for the very first time to be shoved into a cage and endure a nauseating ride of bumps and turns. He ends up in a noisy parking lot full of humans talking to him in high, squeaky tones and trying to pick him up. After waiting for hours in the hot sun, someone finally decides to pick him, and they wrench him unceremoniously away from his loving family.

The car ride to his new home is just as traumatic, except this time he has no one to share in his misery. Once he's in his new environment, his owner tries to offer him food that not only doesn't smell the same, but it doesn't taste like what he ate that morning. His bed doesn't smell right either, and it's a whole lot quieter without his siblings' playful voices.

A few weeks pass, and Milo has finally learned to adjust to his new home. He still misses his family, but he adores his new owner. Only now, he doesn't feel so well. His stomach won't stop cramping, and he feels miserable. Whatever he eats refuses to stay down, and he's decided that he doesn't want to eat anymore because it's just going to come back up anyway.

Milo endures another car ride to a place that smells of alcohol and anal glands. Strange people shove a rod up his tender rear, and after that, a person comes to talk to his owner with unfamiliar words that make his owner very upset. After a tearful good-bye, Milo is taken to the back to endure the sharp prick of a catheter in his leg and several injections before being placed in a cold, dark cage with no towel or blanket to keep him warm - only paper beneath him for fear of spreading the virus to others in the hospital. Poor, sick Milo is all alone now until his next injection or somebody comes by to check his IV.

Now, I've found through my years of experience that the mortality rate for these puppies tends to decrease when you increase the amount of care that they are given. So, please, when one of these cases walks through your door, I recommend that you don't just worry about the chance of contagion. Try to see things through your patient's eyes.

3. The importance of building an estimate

As a veterinary professional, I've learned that an estimate can be your best friend, and it has many benefits for your clinic. While not all clinics see it for what it's worth, those who do utilize it to its full potential. This is especially true in emergency medicine and specialty practices.

When a patient comes through your door needing something more costly than a normal wellness visit, you should consider building an estimate. It can be used for any variety of treatment plans and can be made up in advance for your more common treatments. This way, you are fully prepared with a plan to discuss with the owner. The estimate should include all items pertinent to the case, such as exams, hospitalization, injections, bloodwork, radiographs, and so much more. It should include anything you deem necessary for that particular treatment. Also, don't forget to add in any take-home prescriptions that the patient is going to need and, if necessary, future rechecks for the pet. Whether it is for a surgery, such as an ACL repair, a blood glucose curve, or even treating for pancreatitis, the estimate gives your client a complete rundown of what is needed to care for their pet. When a diagnosis has been made, the entire estimate should be explained to the client before beginning the treatment. In most cases, the client is unprepared for a costly treatment plan, and an estimate can help them understand what steps are necessary for their pet, as well as why. This will give the client a chance to not just see the cost for what you are doing for their pet but to see the benefits. It also gives the client time to ask any questions regarding the intended plan.

Some veterinarians find that a verbal estimate works well with their clientele. However, a written estimate can be used as a legal, binding contract if something goes wrong. It is extremely important that the person who is paying the bill fully understand what the estimate includes. If there is an unlikely circumstance where the client is unavailable at the time the estimate is given, I would recommend that you contact the client and explain the cost and services on the estimate to ensure no confusion.

Furthermore, it is vital that that person sign and date the estimate. If they are not available, have someone get a verbal confirmation and either the veterinarian or a staff member initial to witness the confirmation. This contract should then be kept in the client's record for future reference if needed.

Jennifer Wiseman was born in New York in 1978.. She moved to Tennessee in 1989 with her family. After high school, she attended Columbia State Community College in Columbia, Tennessee, and graduated from the veterinary technician program in 2000. Jennifer worked in several day veterinary practices, which enabled her to improve on her technical skills and encouraged her to handle inventory, as well as teaching her management skills. She is currently working at the Animal Emergency Clinic in Columbia, Tennessee, and is happily utilizing her skills as an emergency technician.

Ann Wortinger   USA

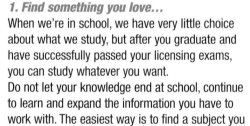

1. Find something you love...

When we're in school, we have very little choice about what we study, but after you graduate and have successfully passed your licensing exams, you can study whatever you want.
Do not let your knowledge end at school, continue to learn and expand the information you have to work with. The easiest way is to find a subject you are passionate about or are even unknowledgeable about and pursue your own education.

For me, nutrition has become my passion. When working in Internal Medicine, we used prescription diets on most of our patients, both in hospital and at home. With the expanding availability of prescription diets and commercial diets, what recommendations to make were sometimes difficult. Rather than just following the manufacturer's guidelines for diet use, I decided to expand my education and learn what the diets were designed to do, and also to learn about the diseases we were managing. By learning about the diseases, many times you can use a diet that was designed for another purpose.

So how do you go about expanding your education? Since I am an avid reader, reading was my tool of choice. Reading allowed me to learn much more information than a commercial, advertisement, or product reference guide could provide. I learned about enzymes and hormones involved in digestion and how these can affect nutrition. Nutrients and ingredients are not the same, and advertisements do not tell you the whole truth.

My education expanded from books to conferences where I would attend every nutrition tract session offered. My choice in reading materials also changed from books to include journal articles and from there it went to writing articles.

There is no quick way to write an article, especially with scientific articles. You need to do research (i.e., more reading), collect your information, develop a plan and outline, and then present your information in a coherent, organized fashion. Then comes the fun part: editing. After having the articles reviewed, there are usually at least three re-writes, some major, some minor. The benefit to me of writing is all that redundancy helps to clarify the information in my head, and increases my understanding of the material.

Many of the topics I write about are selected because I am having difficulty understanding the information, concepts, or disease processes. Writing helps to clarify my understanding, and hopefully passes this information on to other equally confused technicians.

So find something you are REALLY interested in, and put forth the effort to learn all you can. There is the advantage of internet access, web resources, and online classes now, but in my opinion, nothing replaces a good book!

2. Have compassion for both ends of the leash...

Very few of us went into this profession because we wanted to work on or with people. We wanted to work with animals. Very few animals come into a clinic by themselves, and for the precious few who do, none of them are equipped to pay for their veterinary bills. In veterinary medicine, we have to learn to work with the animals at both ends of the leash, even though we are only trained to take care of the four-footed animal on the far end of the leash.

People bring our patients in to the clinic to receive services, they okay our treatment plans, they pay the bills, and, most importantly, they are responsible for following the discharge instructions and administering medications when needed. If we are not able to relate to and explain things effectively to the owners, we will not have the opportunity to work on the animals.

Admittedly, some owners are much easier to work with than others. Unless you work in a very special clinic, you will not be able to decide which owners you get to work with, or what animals you get to work on. You may not always be able to work with the intelligent, young professional who hangs on your every word and has the trained, polite dog.

Sometimes you will get the crabby older person, who has an animal with no training because they do not have the time or energy to do anything with them. We must be able to extend the same level of understanding and care to both clients, and the same level of care to both patients.

I can think of few jobs that would be more fun for me than working at a cat clinic, but that is because I love cats. I love them small and scared, large and furry, and old and crabby, but I can assure you that I can perform just as well with all dogs, and extend the same level of care to them. I can also do a mighty fine job on chickens, rabbits, horses, and sheep. They may not all be my favorites, but I can and do work on them and can explain handling, behavior, and nutrition to owners when needed.

We may not always know what factors have been affecting our clients before they made it into our offices. We've all been in the position where life just seems to be throwing one curve ball after another at us. Are we currently one in a line of many curve balls for them?

Try to offer compassion and care to both of the animals presenting to your practice, and be glad that you only have to work on the four-footed one! We cannot do our jobs without the help of the owners; after all, if they did not care for their pets, we would not have jobs to do.

3. Know your math!!!
Schools teach it, clinics expect you to know it, and the VTNE will test you on it, but math skills remain some of the poorest skills we see in technicians - both new and old.

Why do you think math skills are so important? Without knowing how to do dosage, fluid, and nutrition calculations accurately, our patients can either die or not receive the help we are trying to provide them.

First off, we need to remember the formulas and conversions. A cheat sheet is not illegal, and if this is what you need to use to get the job done correctly, by all means use one! I made conversion and formula cheat sheets for all my students. Being able to be confident in your conversions is essential for correct dosages, and to ensure clients receive the proper information when sending things home, or making adjustments after they are home. Who has not lost a dosage syringe after discharge, or even more fun, what dog has not chewed one beyond usefulness? When we are orally dosing liquid medications, if we remember that each teaspoon is 5 mLs, it is much easier to have a client use this household measure to administer the correct dose of medication should the syringe come up missing or be destroyed. How about explaining to a client that 480 mLs were removed from the abdominal cavity during abdominocentesis - will this mean anything to them? Not nearly as much as telling them that two cups of fluid were removed.

With the epidemic of obesity, are you actually calculating for your clients the caloric intake required for their pets? The recommendations on the bag seldom correlate to what I have calculated, as they are very wide ranges and do not take into consideration any number of factors, including age, activity level, sexual status, or treat intake. Can you accurately calculate daily energy requirements? Are you meeting your patient's actual energy needs or not?

Are your disinfectants being used at their optimal dilutions, are you actually killing the bacteria and viruses you think you are or are you turning them into disinfectant resistant super bugs? Conversely, are you wasting disinfectant by not diluting it enough? Making a disinfectant to a certain color is not accurate or efficient, and you will see that seldom do two people actually make it to the same color, thereby creating different concentrations to work with.

As with most things in our jobs, practice makes perfect. If you allow other people to do your math, that does not help you at all. Many people develop Excel spreadsheets with all their formulas plugged it. While this ensures accuracy in patient treatments, it does nothing for your practice. This is a skill you use daily, and it is your responsibility to ensure you can accurately and confidently do your calculations. While we use fluid pumps to administer most IV fluids, the VTNE is still asking questions regarding drip rates - make sure you can do these problems correctly for both you and your patient's benefit!!

4. Plan for Options
It is very hard when you are just out of school to determine how your life will end up... will you get married, have children, or bring home every "special needs" patient that comes into the clinic? I cannot say that I am the master planner, or that my career has evolved as I laid it out, but I have ensured that I had options available when I did hit a crossroads. To me, few things are more frustrating than not having options, especially when I did not like the options available to me.
I found working in general practice very monotonous and tedious after only one year at work.

Where I was working paid me based on my production - so much for every fecal run, heartworm test conducted, CBC read. To do this, a log book had to be kept and everything I did was logged, talk about tedious! I had a small child at home, and a spouse who also worked. What options did I have? I started to pick up extra hours at a new emergency clinic for extra money and a brain challenge. I did well, and I enjoyed the diversity of cases that presented there. It wasn't too long before I was offered a job full time there with an increase in pay.

When I left my day job, I did not burn any bridges, and have since used this clinic to host externship students when I taught, and asked the staff to be on my advisory board for the veterinary technician program I ran.

From Emergency, I moved to specialty medicine. A veterinarian who had gone to school with me was hired on to work Internal Medicine; 25 years ago, this was not a common thing. Nobody wanted to work with this doctor, since he was seen as difficult. In my mind, I thought, "I have a 2-year-old baby, just how hard could he be?" I spent the next 16 years working with him, and moved to four different hospitals over that time. Each move brought new challenges and new opportunities.

I started writing to increase my knowledge. That led to speaking opportunities, initially just within my hospital, then eventually internationally.

Speaking led to meeting like-minded technicians, and this led to seeking my specialty certification in ECC, then joining the organizing committees for two other specialties, AIMVT and AVNT. Speaking also led to teaching. When I took my first teaching position as the practicum instructor for Clinical Pathology, I did not fully appreciate how well working in Internal Medicine had prepared me for that job. Teaching in a technician program lead to running my own program, and when that was closed down by our corporate owner, I again hit my network and eventually got a job as a hospital administrator.

All of these transitions and changes have occurred because of the choices I made and the people I've met. After 31 years, I'm still a technician, and still learning something new every day!

Ann Wortinger, BIS, LVT, VTS (ECC, SAIM, Nutrition), was born in 1961. She is a 1983 graduate of Michigan State University, and got her specialty certification in Emergency/Critical Care in 2000 and Small Animal Internal Medicine in 2008. She received her specialty certification in Nutrition in 2013.

After graduation, Ann began her career in general practice medicine, but quickly transitioned to emergency/ critical care practice. She has also worked in specialty practice, education, and management. She is currently Hospital Administrator for the Affiliated Veterinary Emergency Service in Allen Park, Michigan.

Ann is active in her state, national, and specialty organizations, serving as a mentor and on a variety of committees and positions. She has more than 40 published articles in various professional magazines, as well as authoring book chapters and a nutrition book for veterinary technicians. Ann has spoken at local, state, national, and international conferences over the past 15 years, as well as teaching online courses at VSPN.

Ann's special love is nutrition, and she expends a significant amount of time and energy learning and teaching and advancing the knowledge of veterinary nutrition. She is especially proud of being able to spend her entire professional career in the veterinary field, and has worked very hard to ensure that she has options available when career changes have been needed or desired.

To maintain a healthy work/life balance, she enjoys spending her off-time in the garden (having earned an Advanced Certified Master Gardener Certificate), reading, and crocheting.

Previously published VetCoach editions

1th edition (2009)

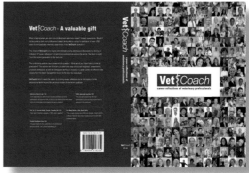

2th edition Europe

3th edition North America

4th edition Latin America

e-book edition (2013)

edition Merial ES

VetCoach books can be ordered via the website **www.vetcoach.info**
The 6th edition VetCoach e-book is available in the Amazon-Kindle store.

Global Professional Veterinary Organizations
World Veterinary Association (WVA), **www.worldvet.org**
World Small Animal Veterinary Association (WSAVA), **www.wsava.org**

Professional Veterinary Organizations Supporting Veterinary Technicians
Academy of Equine Veterinary Nursing Technicians, AEVNT, **www.aaevt.org**
Academy of Internal Medicine for Veterinary Technicians, AIMVT, **www.aimvt.com**
Academy of Veterinary Behavior Technicians, AVBT, **www.avbt.net**
Academy of Veterinary Dental Technicians, AVDTA, **www.avdt.us**
Academy of Veterinary Emergency and Critical Care Technicians, AVECCT, **www.avecct.org**
Academy of Veterinary Nutrition Technicians, AVNT, **www.nutritiontechs.org**
Academy of Veterinary Surgical Technicians, AVST, **www.avst-vts.org**
Academy of Veterinary Technician Anesthetists, AVTA, **www.avta-vts.org**
Academy of Veterinary Technician Clinical Pathology, **www.avcpt.net**
Academy of Veterinary Technicians in Clinical Practice, AVTCP, **www.avtcp.org**
Academy of Veterinary Zoological Medical Technicians, AVZMT, **www.avzmt.org**
American Animal Hospital Association, AAHA, **www.aahanet.org**
American Association of Laboratory Animal Science, AALAS, **www.aalas.org**
American Association of Veterinary State Boards, AAVSB, **www.aavsb.org**
American Society for the Prevention of Cruelty to Animals, ASPCA, **www.aspca.org**
American Veterinary Medical Association, AVMA, **www.avma.org**
CAAHTT/ACTTSA Canadian Association of Animal Health Technologists and Technicians,
CAAHTT, **www.caahtt-acttsa.ca**
Canadian Veterinary Medical Association, CVMA, **www.cvma-acmv.org**
International Veterinary Nurses and Technician Association, IVNTA, **www.ivnta.org**
National Association of Veterinary Technicians in America, NAVTA, **www.navta.org**
Ontario Association of Veterinary Technicians, OAVT, **www.oavt.org**
Veterinary Hospital Managers Association, VHMA, **www.vhma.org**
Veterinary Support Personnel Network, VSPN, **www.vspn.org**

Compassion Fatigue
Fighting Compassion Fatigue in the Veterinary Industry, Katherine Dobbs, RVT, CVMP, PHR,
www.veterinarypracticenews.com/August-2012/Fighting-Compassion-Fatigue-In-The-Veterinary-Industry/
Recognize Symptoms of Compassion Fatigue, Dana Durrance, MA,
http://veterinarynews.dvm360.com/recognize-symptoms-compassion-fatigue

Website and links to other VetTeamCoach project partners
Catalyst Veterinary Practice Consultants, **www.catalystvetpc.com**
VCA Animal Hospitals, **www.vcahospitals.com**

VetCoach, **www.vetcoach.info**

Dr. Selma Abubaker. Police force Sudan

1 year career objectives

1 ....

....

2 ....

....

3 ....

....

5 years career objectives

1 ....

....

2 ....

....

3 ....

....

Overall life and career objectives

1 ....

....

2 ....

....

3 ....

....

Important: Note that you have to review your objectives on an annual basis and depending on the circumstances you may decide to change them

*An act of kindness inspires,
be a drop that creates a ripple.*

Sahaya International, a 501(c)3 non-profit
organization founded by veterinarian Koen Van
Rompay, consists of a growing network of friends
committed to improve the lives of underprivileged
communities in developing countries.

To learn more, get involved, or view the award-winning documentary
"Sahaya Going Beyond" (narrated pro bono by Academy Award winner
Jeremy Irons and with theme song "May it be" by Enya),
visit
www.sahaya.org